Warning!

Violence and the Supernatural

The fictional worlds of Palladium Books® are violent, deadly and filled with supernatural monsters. Other-dimensional beings, often referred to as "demons," torment, stalk and prey on humans. Other alien life forms, monsters, gods and demigods, as well as magic, insanity, and war are all elements in these books.

Some parents may find the violence, magic and supernatural elements of the games inappropriate for young readers/players. We suggest parental discretion.

Please note that none of us at Palladium Books® condone or encourage the occult, the practice of magic, the use of drugs, or violence.

The Rifter® Number 53
Your guide to the Palladium Megaverse®!

First Printing – January 2011

Palladium Online **www.palladiumbooks.com** – Also visit us at Facebook.com/Palladium Books

The Rifter® #53 RPG sourcebook series is published by Palladium Books Inc., 39074 Webb Court, Westland, MI 48185. Printed in the USA.

Palladium Books® Presents:

THE RIF7ER® #53

BRANDT -97

Sourcebook and Guide to the Palladium Megaverse®

Coordinator & Editor in Chief: **Wayne Smith**

Editor: **Alex Marciniszyn**

Contributing Writers:
    James M.G. Cannon
    Steven Dawes
    S.E. Gibbons
    Jeremy M. Hutchins
    Corey Livermore
    Kevin Siembieda
    Damon Sutton
    Michael P. Yocom

Interior Artists:
    Nick Bradshaw
    Kent Burles
    Joseph Lawn
    Allen Manning
    Brian Manning
    Michael Mumah
    Apollo Okamura

Proofreader: **Julius Rosenstein**

Cover Illustration: **Zachary Schoenbaum**

Cover Logo Design: **Steve Edwards**

Credits Page Logo: **Niklas Brandt**

Typesetting & Layout: **Wayne Smith**

Art Direction: **Kevin Siembieda**

Based on the RPG rules, characters,
concepts and Megaverse® created by **Kevin Siembieda**.

  Special Thanks to all our contributors, writers and artists – and a special welcome on board to the artists and writers making their debut this issue. Our apologies to anybody who may have gotten accidentally left out or their name misspelled.

– Kevin Siembieda, 2011

Contents – The Rifter® #53 – January, 2011

conspiracy, and nab the bad guys. All in a day's work for superheroes on the run.

Art by *Michael "No Luck Benjy" Mumah*.

Page 88 – Ravages of Time
– Game Master tips for long Rifts® campaigns

S.E. Gibbons presents ideas, suggestions and techniques for playing through long campaign scenarios like the Coalition Wars®: Siege on Tolkeen™ series (applicable to the Minion War™ and others).

Artwork by *Joseph "New Guy" Lawn*.

Page 92 – The Hammer of the Forge™

Chapter 53: The Two Vulcans is a shocker that will leave you slack-jawed and hungry for the next chapter. Written by *James M.G. Cannon* as he weaves his epic tale set in the Three Galaxies™.

Art by *Apollo "The Transformable" Okamura*.

The Theme for Issue 53

This issue of **The Rifter**® focuses on diverse subject matter, strangeness and talented new contributors. Some issues just seem to come together and this is another one of them. The articles are packed with compelling source material to fill your campaigns with adventure, menaces, monsters, and weirdness.

The Rifter® Needs You

We need new writers and artists to fill the pages of future issues of **The Rifter**® for years to come. You do not need to be a professional writer to contribute to **The Rifter**®. This publication is like a "fanzine" written by fans for fans. A forum in which gamers just like *you* can submit articles, G.M. advice, player tips, house rules, adventures, new magic, new psionics, new super abilities, monsters, villains, high-tech weapons, vehicles, power armor, short works of fiction and more. So think about writing up something short (even something as small as 4-6 pages). Newcomers and regular contributors are always welcomed.

The Rifter® needs new material, especially when it comes to adventures and source material, for *all* of our game lines, especially *Rifts®, Chaos Earth™, Palladium Fantasy RPG®, Heroes Unlimited™, Ninjas and Superspies™, Beyond the Supernatural™, Dead Reign™, Splicers®* and *Nightbane®*.

Pay is lousy, fame is dubious, but you get to share your ideas and adventures with fellow gamers and get four free copies to show to your friends and family.

The Cover

The cover is by **Zach Schoenbaum,** the gent who came in Second Place in Palladium's **2010 Rifter® Art Contest** in the Color/Cover Category. When we needed a superhero cover on short notice, Zach leaped to the challenge. We think it does a nice job representing the *Heroes Unlimited*™ article in this issue. Welcome back, Zach. Keep that imagination burning bright.

Optional and Unofficial Rules & Source Material

Please note that most of the material presented in **The Rifter**® is "unofficial" or "optional" rules and source material.

They are alternative ideas, homespun adventures and material mostly created by fellow gamers and fans like you, the reader. Things one can *elect* to include in one's own campaign or simply enjoy reading about. They are not "official" to the main games or world settings.

As for optional tables and adventures, if they sound cool or fun, use them. If they sound funky, too high-powered or inappropriate for your game, modify them or ignore them completely.

All the material in **The Rifter**® has been included for two reasons: One, because we thought it was imaginative and fun, and two, we thought it would stimulate your imagination with fun ideas and concepts that you can use (if you want to), or which might inspire you to create your own wonders.

www.palladiumbooks.com – Palladium Online

The Rifter® #54

The Rifter® #54 is our Spring issue and will contain all kinds of exciting new source material, 30 Year Anniversary news and other good stuff.
- **Dawn of a New Era, Part Two for Heroes Unlimited™.**
- **Source material for Rifts®.**
- **Source material for numerous settings.**
- **The next chapter of Hammer of the Forge™, fiction.**
- **News, coming attractions and much more.**

Palladium Books® – 30 years of role-playing the infinite possibilities. Limited only by your imagination™

From the Desk of Kevin Siembieda

I guess I should start with the sad news first: My father passed away. Those of you with online access probably already know this, but for some readers of **The Rifter®**, this will be news. It is with a sad heart that I must report my father did not recover as we had hoped.

Henry Dominic Siembieda
December 14, 1930 - October 11, 2010

My dear father passed away due to complications from surgery. As reported last issue, his health was up and down, and he had been on a respirator several times. The prognosis was he would not get significantly better and would be attached to machines for the rest of his life. I knew he didn't want that, and I made the difficult decision to let him slip away with peace and dignity. He will be greatly missed, but cherished always.

The following is a piece I posted in the online *Weekly Update* the week Dad died. It says everything that needs to be said, so I present it here:

I had been struggling for the right words to memorialize my Dad. In some ways he was a very simple man, and in others, quite complex. He only graduated 8th Grade, worked hard most of his life, and missed my mother every day over the 21 years since her death, also from cancer. He enjoyed art and was a decent artist himself, though it frustrated him that he could only draw

in a "cartoon style." He was great at sports, especially baseball and ping pong. He declined being recruited by the Air Force for the Air Force National Baseball Team because it would take him away from his new bride, Florence, too many days of the year. I often wondered how different my father's life might have been had he taken that semi-professional position, but he never wondered about it at all. According to him, he was good, but not that good. He claimed he just happened to be in "the zone" and had a great game when the Air Force recruiting scout saw him play. His teammates used to call him "Unconscious," because Hank would make these amazing "reflex" catches and diving plays in the outfield that seemed to be made without thinking about them. The real reason my Dad was so content with his decision: He had found the love of his life and he was happy to be with her.

Dad was an excellent ping pong player, and playing him made me pretty darn good too. We were roughly equal, and he and I had epic battles and hours of fun at the ping pong table. For those of you reading this and thinking, "Ping pong? That ain't no sport." You've obviously never played the game so hard that you were covered in sweat and had to take a short break between sets. Actually, no matter how tired we were, we rarely took a break. One of my favorite moments with ping pong took place when *John Zinser* of *AEG* came for a visit. I challenged John to a match of ping pong. He informed me that he had been a tennis instructor and semi-pro tennis player, and, well, this was "table tennis" so be prepared to be crushed. Poor John. Someone got crushed, but it wasn't me. He played very well, but he was no *Henry Siembieda*. :)

In conversations with other people about my Dad, folks kept saying how my Dad was "a great man." It made me proud to hear that over and over. He was certainly a great Dad. I think Hank would be surprised to hear so many people say he was "great." My Dad was humble, non-assuming and down to earth. He could be moody and, for a variety of reasons, had a bit of an inferiority complex, but he was pretty great to me and a lot of other people. He lived a hard, simple and honest life. He didn't judge others and tried to treat everyone with respect and fairness. He was usually considerate of others, funny, playful and sometimes outright sweet, yet at the same time he said what he felt. People appreciated that, and liked him for being *so genuine*, even if they didn't like what he might have to say. Most importantly, he was never afraid to show people he loved them. That's a pretty good legacy, if you ask me. The funny part is, my Dad could be a curmudgeon. Hmm, let me rephrase that. I think my Dad *wanted to be* a curmudgeon, and tried to be one on numerous occasions. Only he couldn't pull it off. His kind spirit, sense of fun and good nature leaked out no matter what he did. I actually think that bugged him sometimes. Funny, eh?

As I said, my father would be surprised to find so many people thought he was a great man. I think people forget that you don't have to be rich, powerful or famous to be "great." You can be "great" by living a simple, good and honest life, and affecting others in ways you might not even realize. That was my father.

Yep, my Dad, *Henry Dominic Siembieda*, was a great man. I have countless fond memories of him, and I will never forget him. Heck, I see him standing there with me every time I look in the mirror.

– Kevin Siembieda, October 15, 2010

To everyone's surprise, I've been handling my father's passing quite well. There was a special moment a day after my Dad had died. I was feeling sad and starting to spiral down a dark pit of sorrow and depression. As I was starting down that path, I looked upward and said, "I love you, Dad. I miss you, buddy." Just as I said those words, I rested my hand on the top shelf of a closet and felt something. It was a pair of greeting cards my Dad had given me early in the year. They were hidden away on a top shelf where you couldn't even see them, but my hand fell right on them. One was to "a wonderful son" and outlined how special our relationship was. The other was a birthday card that proclaimed how he only wanted the best for me on that day and every day. Finding those cards at that moment, felt as if Dad was right there speaking to me. It knocked me out of my downward spiral and made me feel loved and at peace. I've been in (reasonably) good spirits and positive mood most of the time since. In fact, that moment helped me find renewed energy and hope for the future. Dad wanted to see Palladium strong again, and I'm going to make it happen. When? Starting now.

A brighter future starts now

Palladium Books® and I have had it pretty rough these last several years. Some of the things you know about, others you don't. The specifics don't really matter, but it has been one obstacle or loss after another for years now. Recently, a business advisor and friend said to me, "I don't know how you've managed to keep the company going through all of this and keep your sanity. I really don't." Hmm. I think some people might wonder about the sane part, but yeah, it has been a wild ride. My Dad used to say something similar every time I gave him an update of recent events, "I don't know how you do it, Kev."

Me either. I guess you just do what you have to do.

I can tell you this: I'm done with death and disaster. I'm done with just treading water and surviving. I'm sick of it, and now that I have my wits about me again, it's time to institute some changes.

For the last two months I've been brainstorming, plotting and planning. I've been talking to friends and freelancers and putting things into place to make *2011* the start of something big. A return to epic role-playing games, sourcebooks and ideas. You've seen glimpses of this over the last couple of years, but Erick Wujcik's death and a number of other losses and setbacks had knocked me out of my game. Sure, we limped along. Sure, we released some excellent product. But we just couldn't maintain the momentum.

2011 will be different.

I've been making moves and putting things into motion behind the scenes that will become apparent throughout 2011. You're already seeing hints of them: Palladium's Facebook page. The Rifts® crossover comic strip in *Heavy Metal® Magazine*. And a number of new products that have created buzz and excitement.

That's only the tip of the iceberg. That energy you feel in the air? That's momentum. And it's building. Barring the unexpected, 2011 will create more excitement with . . .

● More fun with Facebook.

● A dynamic upgrade of the Palladium website.

● Fan favorite titles back in print (see *Coming Attractions* for details on this front. And that starts in *January*).

● The Minion War™ reaches fever pitch with **Megaverse® in Flames**.

● There will be more new **Robotech®** sourcebooks.

● Dynamic new product that pushes the envelope and takes your imaginations to new heights. You'll see more RPG products like **Triax™ 2**, **Heroes of the Megaverse®** and **Dimensional Outbreak™** that will make you want to role-play more than ever.

● More Palladium products released than ever. And we'll be working hard to hit our deadlines.

● Palladium will also be exploring new mediums and venues for marketing, storytelling and gaming.

● 2011 is likely to see Palladium return to *Gen Con*.

Will there be a *Rifts® movie* or *videogame* announced this year? That's entirely out of our hands and we're not waiting around to find out. We'll be looking to market **Rifts®** and all our intellectual properties (I.P.s) wherever we can. Meanwhile, we'll be taking them to new heights of adventure ourselves, in and outside the RPG industry.

Can you feel it? The excitement?

I can. And this is just the beginning. Watch and see what's coming. You won't have to wait long. By the end of February there should be 8-10 out of print titles *back in print*, two new releases, this issue of The Rifter® and a new look to the Palladium website. And that's only the beginning.

Do I have your attention? Good. Stay along for the ride. You won't be disappointed.

– Kevin Siembieda, Publisher

News

By Kevin Siembieda, the guy who should know

Big Plans for 2011

The Palladium crew and I have big plans for the company. We intend to support our new Facebook page, retool the Palladium website in a big way, attend Gen Con, launch a couple of secret projects and, most importantly, release a wide range of new product. In fact, my goal is to release one or two new titles every month. Not only that, but we are pushing the envelope more than ever to create one dynamic new game or sourcebook after another. I'm not even going to hint about some of the secret projects we have boiling in the background. Read on. Be excited. Spread the word. Palladium is going to be producing RPG products that are going to rock your world.

Join Palladium on Facebook

We launched our Facebook page a little before Thanksgiving and Palladium fans around the world are enjoying it.

We had planned to launch our Facebook page in 2011 after we upgraded the Palladium website, but fan pressure to launch sooner prompted us to do so. We're glad everyone is enjoying the Palladium page. We encourage you to join the fun and watch for upcoming special events, photos and features.

New and improved Palladium website is coming soon

We've been wanting to update and improve the Palladium website for some time, but lack of resources, manpower and capital have thwarted our intentions. Now, with some unexpected help from a talented Palladium fan, we hope to have our new and improved website up and running by February sometime. It will be an ongoing work "in progress," but we're very excited about it. **www.palladiumbooks.com**

Gen Con 2011

I haven't made a final decision, but we are leaning heavily toward attending Gen Con this Summer.

Why?

1. It's Palladium Books' 30th Anniversary. Few role-playing game companies ever reach a milestone like that (heck, you can count them on one hand!), so it seems appropriate to celebrate at Gen Con.

2. We heard very good things about last Summer's Gen Con.

3. We haven't been to Gen Con in two years.

4. It seems like time we dropped by again.

Palladium Books holds line on price

Shipping, fuel prices and utilities are all going up. Printing may go up a bit too, as will other costs of operating a business. Our competitors generally charge more (often much more) than Palladium Books does. Yet, Palladium does *not* anticipate raising the prices of its books this year – keeping our products the best bang for your buck.

Hollywood has its eye on Palladium

UPDATE: Rifts® movie. There still isn't any official news about the **Rifts®** movie. For the handful of you who might not know, Palladium Books signed an option agreement with *Walt Disney Pictures* to have *Jerry Bruckheimer Films* develop a live action movie. Eight years later, we're still waiting. First, you must understand that only a tiny percentage of film options ever become movies. Second, the fact that JB Films and Disney have stuck with us for such a long period suggests they really want to make this movie. Third, JB Films is waiting until they get the right script. That's cool, because none of us want to see a bad movie.

Palladium recently had another major, Hollywood film company express an interest in **Rifts®** and they are eyeballing a couple other Palladium I.P.s. Meanwhile, an independent writer/producer had been shopping around **Nightbane®** though nothing seems to have come of his efforts. It would be cool to see any of Palladium's Intellectual Properties (I.P.s) extrapolated into other mediums.

Personally, I think **Rifts®, Nightbane®, Beyond the Supernatural™, Palladium Fantasy®, Dead Reign™, Wormwood™, Phase World®, Skraypers™, After the Bomb®** (animated perhaps), **Splicers®** and, well, most of Palladium's RPG titles, would make a great movie, movie franchise or television show. World building is, after all, our specialty.

Other high powered interest. Did you know that *THQ* and *Bioware* had expressed a possible interest in developing **Rifts®** last year? Yep, exciting stuff. THQ decided to pass (too bad) and Bioware was inquiring about available rights for *possible* future consideration. We're also exploring the possibility of doing *Facebook* games.

Now if only some Hollywood filmmaker or videogame company would pull the trigger and make an awesome movie, TV show or digital game based on one or more of Palladium's I.P.s!

Freelancer Creative Conference

As part of Palladium's big move into a new decade of dynamic games and raw excitement, we are hosting a Creators Conference in April. This is going to be a super-secret (everyone attending must sign an NDA to walk through the door) meeting to discuss Palladium's future, their role in it, game design, writing and new projects, along with some gaming, fun and laughs.

There is high energy and raw excitement among the Palladium staff and freelancers. Expect wonderful RPG products all year long and, with any luck, for years to come.

Trion Settlement

Rift and Rifts®. The lawsuit has been settled. Regrettably, I am not at liberty to discuss any aspect of it. Suffice it to say Palladium's **Rifts®** pen and paper RPG continues as always and we continue to look for licensing partners to bring **Rifts®** to new mediums such as MMOs, videogames, film, toys, etc. It is our understanding that Trion's Rift: Planes of Telara is now titled Rift.

The Minion War™ in 2011

The Minion War™ is the ongoing battle between the denizens of rival Hells, Hades and Dyval. This is all out combat as demons and Deevils try to annihilate each other. Humans and other mortals are caught in the crossfire or recruited as soldiers and supporters.

Rifts® Dimensional Outbreak™ and **Heroes of the Megaverse®** (both available now) were hot items in 2010.

Heroes of the Megaverse® serves as a nice prelude to **Armageddon Unlimited™** as well as a mechanism to introduce super beings into the *Rifts®* and *Phase World®/Three Galaxies™* settings. Each can also be used as a *standalone* sourcebook for **Heroes Unlimited™**, **Rifts®** or **Phase World®/Three Galaxies™**.

Armageddon Unlimited™ is a crossover title in which the demon and Deevil forces battle for dominion of the Earth. But if neither can win, the Deevils intend to decimate the planet. If you enjoy "save the world" scenarios, then this book is a must for you. However, it is a fabulous sourcebook with a wealth of new super abilities, new Power Categories, expanded power categories, magic weapons and more for **Heroes Unlimited™**. Truly epic.

Rifts® Megaverse® in Flames™ carries the Minion War™ to Rifts Earth as the war between demons and Deevils ripples across the Megaverse. Rifts Earth will never be the same and you might think this is the end of the Minion War, but you'd be wrong. A Spring 2011 release.

Rifts® Crossover Comic in Heavy Metal® Magazine

Part One appeared this Fall in the September issue and it was awesome. Part Two should be coming soon. As you may recall, *RC* and *Dominic Aradio* have created a two-part **Rifts®/Colt the Outlander™** crossover comic strip that is appearing in **Heavy Metal® Magazine**. Part Two should appear in an upcoming issue of Heavy Metal early this year (2011). Watch for it.

The Rifter® Subscription Drive

Once a year, Palladium launches a special subscription drive for **The Rifter®** in which you can get a subscription at discount prices and a special gift worth approximately $13-$24. Well, it's that time of year. **The Rifter®** Super-Subscription Offer starts now and runs through February, 2011. See the full description elsewhere in this issue.

2010 Christmas Surprise Packages brought plenty of cheer and good will

Palladium's annual **Christmas Surprise Package** tradition was a big hit again this year. I'm happy to say we put smiles on the faces of many a gamer around the world. Orders came in from across the *USA* and *Canada*, from places such as *England*, *France*, *Spain*, *Denmark*, *Norway* and Germany, and as far away as *Korea* and *Australia*. I hope everyone enjoyed their Surprise Package. Keep those imaginations burning bright and game on.

80+ titles available as PDFs at DriveThruRPG.com

Palladium has made some out of print titles and the first 40 issues of **The Rifter®** available as PDF digital downloads from **DriveThruRPG.com**. We are regularly asked if out of print titles such as **Nightbane® Book Four: Shadows of Light™**, the original **Mechanoids® RPGs, Boxed Nightmares™, BTS First Edition,** etc. are available, and they are, at **DriveThruRPG.com**. Check 'em out.

Coming Attractions

Palladium's 2011 Release Checklist

All January releases are definite. All other dates are tentative, but these are the release dates Palladium is shooting for.

2011 Releases

January
- **Rifts® World Book 20: Canada** – *Back in print*
- **Rifts® Dark Conversions** – *Back in print*
- **Palladium Fantasy RPG®** – *Back in print*
- **Rifts® Game Master Guide** – *Back in print*
- **Rifts® World Book 5: Triax & The NGR** – *Back in print*
- **Rifts® Bionics Sourcebook** – *Back in print*
- **Rifts® China One** – *Back in print*
- **Rifts® Megaverse Builder** – *Back in print*

- **The Rifter® #53** – **New!** Available now.

- **Armageddon Unlimited™** – **New!** January 25, 2011

February
- **Rifts® Dimension Book™ 14: Thundercloud Galaxy™** – **New!** February
- **Rifts® Book of Magic** – *Back in print* – February

And maybe another reprint or two.

New Releases Coming Soon (tentative)
- **Rifts® WB One: Vampire Kingdoms™, Expanded & Updated** (March)
- **Robotech® New Generation™ Sourcebook** (March)
- **Rifts® Vampires Sourcebook™** (March or April)
- **The Rifter® #54** (April)
- **Rifts® Megaverse® in Flames** (Minion War™ crossover; April or May)
- **Dead Reign™ Sourcebook Three**
- **Rifts® World Book™: Lemuria**
- **Rifts® Chaos Earth™: First Responders Sourcebook**
- **The Rifter® #55** (July)

In the Pipeline

- **Robotech® UEEF Marines** and other **Robotech® sourcebooks**.
- **Rifts® sourcebooks**
- **Rifts® Chaos Earth™ sourcebooks**

- Palladium Fantasy® ™: Mysteries of Magic™ Two &
  Three
- Palladium Fantasy® other sourcebooks
- Warpath™ Urban Jungle RPG

And other good stuff. Lots of other good stuff!

Back in print

Palladium Fantasy
Role-Playing Game®

A complete role-playing game set in a unique realm of high fantasy and epic adventure that has thrilled fans for 27 years. All the fantasy elements you'd expect are there, but spun in ways that you may not expect. Magic has replaced science. The elder races of Dwarves, Elves and Titans have given way to the rise of humanity and the Wolfen Empire. While the monster races – Goblins, Orcs, Ogres and Trolls – lay claim to the Old Kingdom, from which they launch their pillaging raids. And that's just the beginning.

- 13 different races available to player characters from human to Wolfen, Changeling, Elf, Dwarf, Ogre, Troll, Goblin, and many others.
- 25 Occupational Character Classes to select from.
- Magic unlike any you've ever seen before.
- 300+ Wizard and Warlock spells.
- 80+ psionic powers.
- 40 magic items plus magic potions, powders and fumes.
- 20 Curses and magical Faerie Foods.
- Summoner and the circles of power and summoning at his command.
- Diabolist and his Runes, Wards and Power Words.
- Mind Mage, Psi-Mystic, Psi-Healer and Psi-Sensitive.
- Poisons, herbs, potions and magic components.
- Men at arms with punch and power.
- Holy Swords and Rune Weapons.
- 100,000 years of history.
- A complete game with *all the rules you need to play* (additional sourcebooks, characters, abilities and settings optional).

- 336 pages – $26.95 retail – Cat. No. 450 – by Kevin Siembieda.
- Back in stock and available now.

Rifts® World Book 20:
Rifts® Canada™

A comprehensive overview of Canada, including notable places, cities, towns, people, O.C.C.s, monsters and conflicts. Though much of Canada has reverted to wilderness, there are pockets of civilization and technology, though not all of them human.

- The Inuit Shaman O.C.C. and abilities.
- 12 Monsters of the North, including Sasquatch and Loup Garou.
- 7 demonic beings including Demon Bears, Windigo and Sedna the Sea Hag.
- 8 D-Bee R.C.C.s common to Canada, including the Cyber-Horsemen of Ixion R.C.C. (bionic Centaurs).
- The Headhunter O.C.C. defined. Includes the Techno-Warrior, Assassin, Anti-Robot Specialist, Techno-Hound, and Momano Headhunter.
- Tundra Ranger O.C.C.s: Ranger, Scout, Cavalry, and Trapper-Woodsman.
- Techno-Wizard Bionics and notable gear of the Tundra Rangers.
- The Canadian frontier mapped and described.
- City of Old Calgary, Fadetowns and notable cities and locations; some with maps of the area.
- Travel rules for snow, ice, and arctic conditions, plus storms, flash floods and other weather events.
- Rules for hypothermia and exposure.
- 192 pages – $24.95 retail – Cat. No. 835 – by Kevin Siembieda.
- Back in stock and available now.

Rifts® Dark Conversions™

The focus of Dark Conversions™ is on creatures of darkness and other monsters such as Alien Intelligences, Elementals, were-beasts, vampires, weird supernatural beings, Elementals, the Nightbane and others. If you are looking for practitioners of

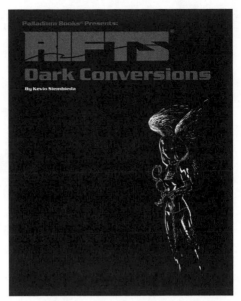

dark magic, villains, monsters and vile horrors to pit against your heroes, this is the sourcebook for *you*. Many creatures also have notes on how they fit into the Rifts Earth setting and where they may be encountered.

- **130 monsters statted out and described for your inclusion in Rifts®, Chaos Earth™, Phase World® or any Mega-Damage setting.**
- **Were-Beasts, Gremlins, Gargoyles and spirits.**
- **Undead legions, Demon and Deevil hordes from the world of *Palladium Fantasy RPG®*.**
- **Conversions for the Nightbane® and the Nightlords™ and their minions.**
- **Alien Intelligence creation rules and tables.**
- **Elemental beings of lesser and greater stature.**
- **Entities and monsters from Beyond the Supernatural™.**
- **Dark Magic: Witches, Shifters, Diabolists, and Summoners.**
- **192 pages – $24.95 retail – Cat. No. 852 – by Siembieda & others.**
- **Back in stock and available now.**

Rifts® Game Master Guide

The ultimate Rifts® reference and sourcebook, it contains *all* the weapons, equipment, body armor, power armor, robots, vehicles, skills and psionics from *Rifts® World Books 1-23, Sourcebooks 1-4,* and *Siege on Tolkeen 1-6,* collected into one big reference. Plus, maps, lists and indexes of O.C.C.s, R.C.C.s, experience tables and more.

- **503 weapons, including explosives, plus E-Clips and ammo notes.**
- **300 skills listed and described.**
- **290 pieces of equipment.**
- **104 suits of body armor.**
- **182 vehicles.**
- **86 suit of Power Armor.**
- **58 robots.**
- **Optional combat rules and examples of play.**
- **Comprehensive index of O.C.C.s, R.C.C.s, P.C.C.s, and Monsters.**
- **Experience tables for scores of character classes.**
- **Designer notes, rules clarifications and reference notes.**

- **Game Master tips and hints for running Rifts®.**
- **Maps, adventure ideas, and a lexicon of terms.**
- **352 pages of reference material galore.**
- **Cover by David Dorman. Interior art by Perez, Wilson & others.**
- **352 pages – $26.95 retail – Cat. No. 845.**
- **Back in stock and available now.**

Rifts® Bionics Sourcebook™

A compendium of bionic and cybernetic systems in the Rifts North America setting, with information about partial and full conversion cyborgs, Headhunters, City Rats, the Cyber-Doc and more. A must-have resource for fans of cyborgs.

- **220+ bionic components and features plus foreign bionics.**
- **47 Commercial Cybernetic implants and 24 Black Market bionics.**
- **7 different City Rat O.C.C.s and insight to life in the 'Burbs.**
- **The Cyber-Doc O.C.C. explored in more depth.**
- **The Cyber-Snatcher Villain O.C.C. dealing in "previously owned" bionics and cybernetics. Want to guess how they come by these parts?**
- **The Cyborg O.C.C. revisited plus rules & info on repairing bionics.**
- **TW Bionics, cybernetics to inhibit magic and more.**
- **112 pages – $16.95 retail – Cat. No. 850 – by Kevin Siembieda.**
- **Back in stock and available now.**

Rifts® World Book Five:
Triax and the NGR™

The New German Republic (NGR) is surrounded and besieged by the hostile Gargoyle Empire – an empire of giant monsters. Only the superior robotics and weapons technology of Triax

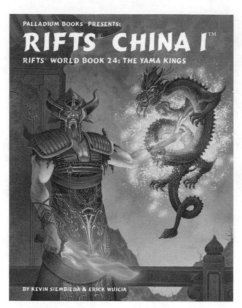

keeps the monsters at bay, but for how long? This epic World Book presents the Triax robots, power armor, cyborgs, and world setting that is Rifts Germany and surrounding region. More than 100,000 copies sold!

- 35+ weapons and explosives, plus body armor and other gear.
- 19 combat vehicles from tanks to jet aircraft.
- 12 Triax giant robot suits and vehicles.
- 9 other types of Triax robots and drones.
- 8 Triax Cyborgs plus bionic components.
- Triax power armor units including the T-550 Glitter Boy.
- 11 NGR Military O.C.C.s.
- The Euro-Juicer and designer drugs.
- Gypsy O.C.C.s and their special abilities.
- The Gargoyle Empire and its technology and war machines.
- 21 notable weapons of the Gargoyle Empire and 4 R.C.C.s.
- Setting and regional overview, Brodkil, Gene-Splicers and more.
- Cover and art by Kevin Long. 13 pages of comic book story.
- 224 pages – $24.95 retail – Cat. No. 810 – by Kevin Siembieda.
- Back in stock and available now.

Note: For dozens of new weapons, armor, robots, drones, power armor suits, cyborgs, vehicles and updated information about the NGR, Triax and the war, see **Rifts® World Book 31: Triax™ 2** – 192 pages – $24.95 – Cat. No. 881.

Rifts® World Book 24:
Rifts® China One

There is no place on Rifts Earth more exotic, magical and dangerous than China, especially since the Hell of the Yama Kings has bled into the mortal plane.

- 33 Chinese Demons, including Yaksha the Tiger and the Naga.
- 8 Chinese Goblins and the Naga-Spawn (semi-divine humans).
- 5 Chinese Ghosts, plus the Terra-Cotta Warriors.

- 24 Demonic curses.
- 11 provinces and the Yama Kings who rule them.
- The eight Hells on Earth.
- The Dragonlands, the Ghost City, Qingping Market, City of the Future, Wuchang, and many other notable places.
- World overview, maps and adventure ideas galore.
- 160 pages – $20.95 retail – Cat. No. 857 – by Wujcik & Siembieda.
- Back in stock and available now.

Note: For 18 new O.C.C.s, heroes of the Celestial Court, Geofront, secret technology, mystical powers, Demon Wrestling, Demon Quelling, Chi Weapons, martial arts and more, see **Rifts® World Book 25: Rifts® China 2** – 160 pages – $20.95 – Cat. No. 858.

Rifts® Dimension Book™ 7:
Megaverse® Builder

Your guide to creating your own corner of the infinite Megaverse®. The big picture of how the Megaverse® works, plus rules and suggestions for creating your own dimension.

- Dimension creation rules.
- Dimensional storms and anomalies.
- Dimensional monsters and travelers.
- The dimensions of Spires, the Great Machine, and the Garbage Pit.
- Dozens of Hook, Line and Sinker™ adventure outlines and ideas for many more.
- The Shifter O.C.C. expanded, exotic familiars & summoning table.
- Tolkeen Artifact Hunter O.C.C. and Scavenger O.C.C.
- Designer notes, suggestions, tips & hints for dimension building.
- 96 pages – $16.95 retail – Cat. No. 859 – by Carl Gleba.
- Back in stock and available now.

Rifts® Book of Magic

The ultimate Rifts® reference on magic

This is it, the ultimate guide to magic for Rifts Earth. All the magic spells, magic tattoos, Techno-Wizard items, magic weap-

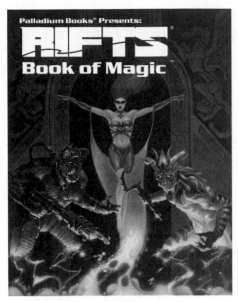

Palladium Books® Presents:

RIFTS®
Book of Magic

ons, equipment, body armor, restraints, parasites, symbiotes, magic items, Bio-Borgs, armor, automatons, Iron Juggernauts, and more from *Rifts® World Books 1-23 Sourcebooks 1-4,* and *Siege on Tolkeen 1-6,* collected into one big reference.

- 850+ spells of great variety.
- 370+ magic items, weapons and devices.
- Elemental Magic, Temporal Magic, Ley Line Magic, Cloud Magic and Necromancy.
- Tattoo Magic, Nazca Line Magic, Nature Magic, Whale-songs and Ocean Magic, and more.
- Magic Songs, Chants, Biomancy, Magic Herbs, and Iron Juggernauts.
- Techno-Wizard weapons and devices, Rune weapons, Millennium Tree wands and other magic items.
- Magic herbs, plants, components and Symbiotes.
- Shamanistic magic, Fetishes, Talismans and more.
- Comprehensive index of Practitioners of Magic.
- Designer notes, comments, tips & hints for running magic characters.
- 352 pages – $26.95 retail – Cat. No. 848 – Siembieda and others.
- February 2011 back in print.

NEW titles coming soon

Armageddon Unlimited™

For Heroes Unlimited™ – Ships January, 2011

Demons and Deevils are fighting for dominance of the Earth, and if they can't win, nobody can have it. They'll destroy the planet.

Armageddon Unlimited™ is the ultimate good vs evil setting and adventure. The fate of the world hangs in the balance and only you can stop its destruction.

Armageddon Unlimited™ is more than an epic world-saving adventure, it is also a sourcebook jam-packed with new powers, magic, weapons and Power Categories that can be incorporated into any *Heroes Unlimited™* campaign.

Highlights include:
- 7 new Minor and 14 Major Super Abilities.

- Deevil and Demon magical Chaos Weapons.
- Enchanted Weapons of Order.
- Demon Hunter Power Category and abilities, 'nuff said.
- Crusader of Light Power Category and abilities allow you to play a Champion of Light.
- Heroic Hellion Power Category and abilities allow you to play a "reformed demon."
- Magically Bestowed Variant Power Categories and abilities let you wield weapons that empower good and destroy evil.
- Demonic monster creation table.
- More than a dozen NPC villains.
- Arcane orders, secret societies, and magic guilds.
- The Chaos Generator and the threat of Armageddon.
- A menagerie of evil villains, people and places.
- The Armageddon scenario and adventure ideas.
- Written by Carl Gleba. Additional text by Kevin Siembieda.
- Cover by John Zeleznik.
- 160 pages – $20.95 retail – Cat. No. 527. January 2011 release.

Rifts® Dimension Book™ 14:
Thundercloud Galaxy™

The **Thundercloud Galaxy™** is the perfect companion to **Rifts® Dimensional Outbreak™** to expand one's gaming Megaverse in the Three Galaxies. History, aliens, weapons, spacecraft, and adventure in a galaxy far, far away.

- The galaxy described; history and time-line.
- 16 new alien R.C.C.s, plus notes on the Exiles and Dominators.

- 6 new O.C.C.s.
- Monster and Animal Creation Tables.
- Guidelines for Magic Weapon Making.
- Notable weapons and technology.
- Notable organizations and secret societies.
- The Trensik Mercenaries.
- The Vortex Region.
- The Splugorth Kingdom of Desslyth and many other notable worlds.
- New worlds of adventure.
- Written by Braden Campbell. Art by Michael Mumah.
- 160 pages – $20.95 retail – Cat. No. 883. February 2011.

Rifts® World Book One:
Vampire Kingdoms™,
Expanded & Updated

Kevin Siembieda is reorganizing, tweaking, expanding and updating one of the most popular **Rifts® World Books** ever published: **Vampire Kingdoms™**. This will include *some* new artwork and an expanded page count. The book will be updated and expanded in much the same way as Kevin did with **Rifts® Sourcebook One** a few years ago. Best of all, it will be accompanied by the **Rifts® Vampires Sourcebook™**.

- The observations of Doc Reid.
- Vampires: Their strengths, weaknesses and powers.
- The Vampire Kingdoms expanded.
- Vampire strategies and plans for conquest.
- Vampire hunters and Techno-Wizard slayer devices (new and old).
- Key locations including Juarez and El Paso.
- The mystery of the Yucatan Peninsula.
- Traveling Shows, Freak Shows and Circuses.
- Monsters, D-Bees, and adventure ideas galore.
- Updated and revised to 110 P.A.
- Cover by E.M. Gist. Interior art by various artists.
- Written by Kevin Siembieda.
- 192 to 224 pages – $24.95 retail – Cat. No. 802-E. March 2011. release.

Rifts® Vampires Sourcebook™

All new source material

Trouble is stirring in the Vampire Kingdoms as ambitious vampire lords, ladies and misanthropes seek to expand their power to dominate more mortal life forms.

Written by Kevin Siembieda and a handpicked selection of other writers, this sourcebook explores the vampires of Mexico and their kingdoms in ways you never imagined. Tons of new data, adventure ideas and revelations.

- Vampire protectors and guardians.
- Vampire rogues, mercenaries and warlords.
- Vampire operations away from the Kingdoms.
- Vampire incursions along the southern borderlands.
- New vampire hunters and human strongholds.
- Vampire hunter "exterminators."
- Frightful revelations, secrets, and adventure ideas.
- And much, much more.
- Cover by Michael C. Hayes. Interior art by various artists.
- Written by Kevin Siembieda, Braden Campbell and Mark Dudley.
- 128 pages – $16.95 retail – Cat. No. 884. Spring 2011.

Robotech®
New Generation™ Sourcebook

This Robotech® sourcebook will be an early 2011 release.
- Rules for using mecha, power armor and technology from all four eras of Robotech.
- Kit-bashed mecha and rules for jury-rigging and combining parts from different generations of mecha.
- Freedom Fighter O.C.C.s and resistance organizations.
- Rogues and misfits from the three Robotech Wars.
- New weapons, vehicles, mecha and more.
- Villains, traitors, bandits, Invid henchmen, adventure and adventure ideas galore.
- Written by Kevin Siembieda and Irvin Jackson.
- A "manga" size sourcebook.

- 192-256 pages – $16.95 retail – Cat. No. 554. Final page count and price may be subject to change. Spring 2011.

Rifts® World Book: Lemuria™

At last, the underwater realm of Lemuria. The people and history of Lemuria, new magic, sea herbs and healing, sea monsters, and more.

- The Lemurians, their race, history and society.
- New O.C.C.s including the Serpent Hunter, Shriekers, Oceanic Guardsman, Aquatic Biomancer and others.
- The Stone Guardians of Easter Island and other mysteries.
- Biomancer Gardens and Aquatic Biomancy.
- Bio-Armor, Bio-Weapons and Bio-Construct Symbiotes.
- New psionic abilities.
- Sea Serpents, monsters, adventure ideas, and more.
- Written by Greg Diaczyk.
- 160 pages – $20.95 retail – Cat. No. 885. Final page count and price may be subject to expansion and increase. Spring 2011.

Rifts® Megaverse® in Flames™

The Minion War spills across Rifts Earth, where demons and infernals hope to recruit allies and use the Rifts as gateways of destruction. Their influence shakes things up across the planet, especially at locations where demons and Deevils already have a strong presence. More details to follow, but for now, 'nuff said.

- Soulmancer and Blood Magic.
- The Seven Deadly Plagues.
- The Demon Plagues across the globe.
- Battleground: Earth – as demons and infernals amass their legions.
- Rifts Calgary – also known as Hell's Pit; the kingdom described.
- Ciudad de Diablo, Harpies' Island and other notable Hell holes on Earth.
- Lord Doom, Pain and other demonic leaders.
- Horune treachery, Dimension Stormers and other villains.
- Global chaos and the places most dramatically affected by the Demon Plagues.
- Notable demonic Generals, mercenaries, people and places.
- Many adventure ideas.
- Written by Carl Gleba.
- 192 pages – $24.95 retail – Cat. No. 876. Spring 2011.

Rifts® Chaos Earth™ Sourcebook:

First Responders

Data about the chaos and madness of the early days of the Great Cataclysm, and the brave men and women who tried to stem the tide of destruction and save lives, the First Responders.

- Apocalypse Plagues: Strange diseases, symbiotes and mutations that transform, torment, harm and kill Earth's survivors.
- First Responder O.C.C.s, skills and special equipment.
- Civilian O.C.C.s, skills and orientation.

- Notable rescue vehicles, robot drones, and technology.
- New weapons, vehicles, mecha and more.
- Character modification and enhancement rules.
- Creatures from the Rifts and adventure ideas galore.
- Written by Jason Richards & Kevin Siembieda.
- 96 to 128 pages – $16.95 retail – Cat. No. 665. Coming in 2011.

bradshaw
2010

Check out Palladium's website –
www.palladiumbooks.com –
for updates, news and other information.

The Rifter®
Super-Subscription Offer

- **Free gift**
- **Free shipping in the USA**
- **Delivered to your door**
- **A Megaverse® of Adventure and Fun!**

The Rifter® is a quarterly sourcebook series for the entire Palladium Megaverse®. It is written by fans and up and coming writers, for fans. Some, like #4, #8, #19, #20-26, #28-35, #38, #40, and others have even become coveted *collector's items* that command big bucks! (For a while, people were reportedly paying as much as $70 online for #21.)

Each issue of **The Rifter®** presents unofficial and/or official adventures, characters, powers, weapons, equipment and fiction for *Rifts®, Heroes Unlimited™, Palladium Fantasy RPG®, Chaos Earth™, Splicers®, Nightbane®, Beyond the Supernatural™, Dead Reign™,* and/or any variety of other Palladium games and world settings. It's also a place to get the latest news, product release info, and see new games showcased.

The Rifter® is more than a magazine or sourcebook, it is a forum for *new talent*. Imaginative "fan" and semi-professional writers and artists submit their work for consideration and see their creations brought to life and shared with thousands of other Palladium fans. (And get paid for it too!) Palladium uses **The Rifter®** to try new talent with an eye toward future, bigger projects. *Carl Gleba, Todd Yoho, Jason Richards, Brandon Aten, Jason Marker, Apollo Okamura, Brian Manning* and others all got their start in the pages of **The Rifter®**.

In short, if you're into one or more of Palladium's role-playing games and like to explore new realms of possibility, then **The Rifter®** is for you.

Super-Subscription Offer

The cover price of **The Rifter®** is **$11.95** – a steal for 96 pages of RPG source material and adventures – but a subscription gets you **The Rifter®** delivered to your doorstep and you can select a *free gift worth $13-$23* (available *only* during this special offer, for the cost of shipping and handling). All prices are in U.S. dollars.

- **$39.80 – USA. That's only $9.95 each,** a savings of $8.00, and Palladium pays the shipping! Plus you get to select a FREE subscriber's gift worth $13-$23 (please include $5.00 to cover shipping and handling). That's *$44.80 total* including shipping and handling for the gift. **Note:** This rate and gift is *limited* to subscribers in the *USA only.* Sorry.
- **$61.80 – Canada. That's $15.45** for each issue of **The Rifter®,** plus you get to select the FREE subscriber's gift (please include $8.00 to cover shipping and handling). That's *$69.80*

including the gift item. That's still not a bad price for a 96 page sourcebook. Our apologies on the higher cost, but Palladium Books can no longer cover the increased cost of postage to other countries. We hope you understand.

- **$73.80 – Overseas. That's $18.95** for each 96 page issue, plus you get to select a FREE subscriber's gift (please include $13.00 to cover shipping and handling). That's *$86.80* including the gift item. We are only passing along the additional postage cost, but it is hefty. Our apologies. Postal rates are out of our hands.

Note: Please indicate if the gift item is NOT wanted. You may decline the gift and get your subscription for the regular price of $39.80 (USA), $61.80 (Canada) or $73.80 (other country).

A FREE gift worth $13-$40

You pay only the cost of shipping and handling ($5.00 in the USA, $8.00 Canada, $13.00 overseas).

Gift choice #1: Best of The Rifter® ($12.95 value, signed by Kevin Siembieda and available Palladium staff).

Gift choice #2: The Rifter® #14 and **#15** ($23.90 value at current cover price, both are out of print).

Gift choice #3: Rifts® Machinations of Doom™; Sourcebook & Graphic Novel ($18.95 value).

Gift choice #4: Rifts® World Book 19: Australia ($24.95 value).

Gift choice #5: Palladium Fantasy RPG® Book 14: Land of the Damned One – Chaos Lands ($24.95 value; northern monsters and more).

Gift choice #6: The Book of Weapons & Armor and **The Book of Weapons & Castles** ($19 value; while supplies last).

- **IMPORTANT NOTE:** Please enclose shipping and handling to receive your FREE gift: $5.00 in the USA, $8.00 Canada, $13.00 overseas. Thank you. You can *decline* the free gift and pay only the subscription price if you wish.
- **Indicate what issue number you'd like your new subscription to start at:** #52 (last issue), #53 (this current issue), #54 (next issue, April 2011), or when your current subscription ends.
- **How to order.** *Send mail orders* with a check or money order (for *$44.80* – including handling & shipping of free gift in the *USA*) to:

The Rifter® Subscription Dept.
39074 Webb Court – Westland, MI 48185-7606

Credit Card orders can be made online *(www.palladiumbooks.com)* or by telephone 734-721-2903 (this is an order line *only*). Order today! And tell a friend! Tell lots of friends!!

Offer good only thru February 28, 2011

The Lucky Psychic

An Optional New P.C.C. for Beyond the Supernatural™, 2nd Ed.

By Steven Dawes

"I could tell you all I know about what the eggheads in the labs coats call the 'Chaos Theory' and its applied physics and mathematics and whatnot, but all that would prove is how great of a cure it is for insomnia. I imagine that you've at least heard of it before, right? You've seen the movie 'Jurassic Park' before, right? Remember that chaos theorist guy, 'Ian Malcolm'? Remember how he referred to himself as a 'chaotician'? Remember how he correctly calculated that the park was gonna go straight to hell based on how the management ran the place? Well that's the basic idea behind the 'Chaos Theory'; that the simplest changes in initial conditions can yield widely diverging outcomes. And as for me, you could say that I'm a 'chaotician' myself, but there's more to my talents than calculating the worst possible outcomes that will happen at the worst possible times.

"The long and short of what I do is that I can adjust, alter and outright change the probabilities, chances and odds of the events happening around me. In short, I make my own luck. Oh sure, every Joe makes his own luck and has a lucky day here and there, but I can call the shots with my luck. It's like Lady Luck and I got an understanding; she always has her say so, but sometimes I get to interject where my luck's concerned. Get it? Got It!

"On a normal day, I've been known to pull off a few pretty neat tricks. For example, I've been able to flip a coin and make it land "tails" several times in a row, I've pulled the top prize winning scratch card from a stack a few times, I win more often than I lose at the craps tables in Vegas, and I've gotten phone numbers from girls that normally wouldn't look at me twice. I think that last part is just my good looks and winning personality. So while I've been known to show off at times (especially when I have a few brewskis swimming around in me), in reality these stunts only make me look like a lucky guy in a city of losers.

"But when the supernatural is lurking about? Oh, now this is when it gets interesting. I've been able to pull off all sorts of chance occurrences in my favor, many of them against my supernatural foe. Some of my more subtle moments have been tripping up some mangy monster while it was charging at me or causing its attack to come up short and miss me entirely. Some of my more impressive moments? How about that I've dodged more claws and teeth than I can count? Or that I've performed some spectacular shooting and fisticuffs when I shouldn't have had a snowball's chance in hell. Or that I've taken some beastly bashings on the chin from supernatural baddies that could've leveled a building with their ridiculous amounts of strength, and walked away with only some ugly bruises to show for it.

"You know, this monster once hurled a car on top of me and should have flattened me. But as my luck would have it, the car just happened to be a convertible and the top was down so when the creature tried to squash my prone body, it landed upside down over me to where my body was perfectly safe and unharmed in the space between the front seat and the dash board! I mean dude... I should be an action movie hero when I can pull off stunts like that!

"And how do I do these things? Well, I don't know exactly. But for one thing, I've always had a great head for numbers and calculating, and I think that's part of it. For example, you see this pair of dice I just yanked outta my pocket? Well, did you know that rolling two 6-sided dice twenty five times has a probability of .505532 that you'll roll a Snake Eyes at least once? I didn't memorize that or anything; it just happens like that, a lot. I notice the small details and I recognize the mathematical probabilities of different outcomes in the initial conditions of my surroundings just by slightly changing those conditions.

"But there's more to it than the number crunching. I think there's some psychic manipulation of the physical stuff around me that's either working in tandem with my inner number crunching, or it goes into action because of them. While sometimes I can consciously work the small stuff like the dice and coins, the bigger things like that convertible safely landing over me... that's something that just happens sometimes. This psychic guy once told me that I probably made that outcome happen on an 'intuitive' level or something like that. Of course I retorted by explaining to him the statistical chances of that exact outcome happening to me and it could have just played out that way. I think he dozed off about halfway through my explanation.

"So while I'm a gambling man who loves to take chances and push my luck, I ain't nobody's fool but my own. I know better than any schmuck alive that luck only gets a man so far. I've botched plenty of cool stunts & tricks that I've tried to pull off. Sometimes they just embarrass me, other times they've put me in downright dangerous predicaments. As tempting as it might be, I don't always go for the long shots or go barreling into whatever, *hoping that my luck will get me back out alive and in one piece. Sometimes a well calculated plan of action can do more than all the luck in the world. And like I said, I'm pretty damn good at calculating.*

"Then again, whatever it is I'm doing, I'm doing it with confidence that the odds are in my favor and Lady Luck will be on my side. Probably."

– Eddie "Bet da' House" Champman

People have always spoken of "luck" as if it were some kind of ethereal, intangible force and yet a very real, autonomous power that seems to pick and choose favorites on some cosmic level. In fact, a lot of people refer to "her" as "Lady Luck." You hear people talk about their supposed luck (or lack of it) all the time, like "He's the luckiest guy I know." or "She's got the worst luck with men." or "Dude, you're lucky you were wearing a seat-belt." Lots of cultures not only believe in the random chance of blind luck, they also believe that by performing various traditions and customs (like kissing horseshoes, dropping coins in wishing wells or painting pin-up girls on the nose of their aircraft), or carrying certain items around with them (like a rabbit's foot, four-leaf clovers, horseshoes or any of the other goodies you find in a box of Lucky Charms cereal), or even spotting or finding something (like a lucky penny or seeing a rainbow) will bring them good luck. Even certain numbers are considered lucky in some cultures, like the number 7 in many western civilizations or the number 8 in the Chinese cultures.

And everyone knows there are things you shouldn't ever do to avoid getting bad luck. How many times have you refused to walk under a ladder? Or wouldn't let a black cat cross your path? Do you always take a pinch off the pile of salt you just spilled and throw it over your shoulder? Are you counting down the days when your seven years of bad luck are over from breaking that old mirror? And heaven forbid that you do anything remotely dangerous or foolhardy on Friday the 13th! Point is, to this day many people still carry a lot of irrational superstitions to avoid doing things they consider unlucky. Are these all really just the last remnants of a superstitious age which we're still brought up to believe in? Is it all really just a silly method of our trying to cope with moments of the unpredictable chance events that we had no control over? Or is there a rational way of explaining the good and bad chance occurrences that befall us all?

There have been numerous attempts by scientific minds over the years that have been applying mathematics, physics and even philosophy to come up with a set of unique terms and theories. These theories have become the metaphoric next-door neighbors of "Lady Luck," such as "reliability," the "probability theory" and the "chaos theory." Of course, fully understanding these theories requires an advanced knowledge of sciences like semiclassical & quantum physics, a vast array of mathematics and dynamical systems that usually confuse the everyday man when you try to explain it to them. There is a popular phrase called "The Butterfly Effect," which basically states that "a butterfly's wings can create tiny changes in the atmosphere that can alter, delay or even create tornadoes in a certain location," which is a much more understandable way of describing the basic theory to people. But even this is a metaphor for the sensitivity of initial conditions that can be altered by small differences or changes in their environment. It is, however, probably the best way to describe the Lucky Psychic.

This psychic class is considered by many to be an ironic mix between the *Genius P.C.C.* and *a Physical Psychic P.C.C.*, whose area of aptitudes includes mathematics and science while his or her aptitude for Physical Psionic abilities directly impacts the physical world. Both of these traits seem to rely on and draw upon one another, working in unison. Perhaps most importantly, the psychic has an intuitive ability to recognize and know the probability of the random occurrences and chance events in the conditions of the environment around him. Even more interesting, he can alter, delay, halt and even create small changes in these conditions to improve the chances of an outcome that's desirable to the psychic.

How this happens is mostly a mystery, even to the psychic. A common belief amongst the parapsychologist community is that the Lucky Psychic's mind is a constantly calculating computer that uses a variety of mathematics, an immense understanding of dynamic physics and other scientific principles to determine the chances of random events that could potentially take place around him. In most cases the psychic is unaware that he's even doing this. The union of his remarkable mental agility with his limited use of various Physical Psionics, like Telekinesis, Ectoplasm, Electrokinesis, Hydrokinesis, Levitation, Leidenfrost Effect and others, is the heart & soul off his "luck." It's believed that the uses of these Physical Psionics are slight and subdued, performed (subconsciously) to manipulate the probabilities and potential random occurrences that affect his environment. It should be noted that while the psychic seems to use the vast majority of physical related psionics in subtle ways, he will not actually possess most of those dedicated psionic abilities to call upon at will like a Physical Psychic. For example, he might be able to alter the chances of a coin landing "tails" via a limited form of Telekinesis even though he lacks the Telekinesis ability itself.

The possibilities of this psychic's talents are really only limited by his environment. Some examples of altering the outcome of performing a skill includes causing a wrench to slip out of a mechanic's hands, a singer could breathe in dust and cough or choke in the middle of a song, or a thief's lock pick tool could bend and break while attempting to pick a lock. Instead of being trampled by a horse himself, the Lucky Psychic could cause the rider to slip and fall off the horse while charging. Instead of a driver running over the psychic, his car could unexpectedly slide out of control (and possibly crash). Or someone could be distracted by some small, random action that causes him to not find or notice the hidden contraband he was looking for, or misread the text of a spell, or incorrectly calculate the mathematical equation he was working on.

These same talents can just as easily create a variety of chance events during combat situations. An enemy could suddenly lose his grip on a weapon and drop it. A slight but sudden gust of wind, or a sudden eye twitch from an unexpected flash of light, or slightly levitating the gun for an instant could cause an enemy to aim too high or too far to the left or right and miss his target. A running/charging enemy could slip and fall on a wet or loose patch of grass, a stone or a rug. Again, keep in mind that the majority of these actions take place without the psychic deliberately planning to make these "freak occurrences" happen. To the Lucky Psychic, these chance events simply happen around him, usually at times when he needed/desired them the most.

It's interesting to note that there are two common personality types with the Lucky Psychic, depending on which aspect of their talents they associate themselves with. The more introverted or *intellectual* types tend to come off as analytical, deductive, calculating and carefully planning in their actions. They enjoy studying and learning a variety of skills (especially science related) and tend to come off as number crunching, statistical "nerds" who love to share their knowledge of physics, mathematics, statistics, probability and even the philosophy of how and why a particular event happened. Those who enjoy the physical aspect of their nature are usually more action-oriented and tend to be daring, self confident types who live by the seat of their pants; sometimes to the point of taking unnecessary risks and being a showoff. They enjoy pressing their luck and many are gamblers who love to play the odds (and stack them in their favor when they can).

The Lucky Psychic's involvement with the paranormal also usually depends on which talents they favor. The intellectual types find that the supernatural blatantly defies every law of science they have ever come to understand, and this intrigues them to no end. "They exist when they should not" is usually enough of a realization for them to join the Lazlo Society or a group of paranormal investigators. While the irony of their being psychic (and therefore defying their own known laws of nature) is not lost on them, but their psychic talents still make some sense in that they are bound by the laws of physics and perform actions and create reactions that can be explained by scientific principles. The supernatural, however, provide no explanation or logic to their existence. So how can/do they exist? That question will only inevitably create more questions which will keep them researching and learning for a lifetime as they'll most likely never find the answers.

For the action-oriented types, they are just as intrigued with the supernatural, but for different reasons. For them, it's the fascinating aspect of the supernatural "adrenaline rush" that makes their talents that much more potent and flamboyant. It's mind-boggling to them that while they can only occasionally perform the slightest of tricks and minimally affect the probabilities around them on a normal day, they suddenly feel "extremely lucky" (via the psychic adrenaline rush) and can pull off some amazing psychic feats and tricks while in the presence of the supernatural (although they are never as dynamic as a Physical Psychic), as well as their intuitive luck altering. While they do realize the unnatural, illogical or unscientific nature of the supernatural, they are more interested in using their talents against them. It's a chance not only to combat the supernatural evils of the world; it's a chance to show off and look good while doing it! Imagine the laughs of causing a Hell Hound to slip and fall while chasing you! Or imagine a zombie swinging a club at you, only to somehow misjudge his swing and miss you, or hit one of his own allies instead. Or imagine a security light suddenly switching on, negating the shadow in which a Devil Ghost was hiding. Or having a laugh as a Death Weaver gets caught up in its own webbing. Now that's talent and fun times, baby!

Of course, there's the drawback of the character's *Potential Psychic Energy* being diverted into two areas of development. The character will never fully attain the mental aptitudes of a *Genius P.C.C.*, as his exceptional skills are limited to the realm of science and mathematics. However, this is not usually viewed as a liability to them, as the character was probably already into the science field as much as he was into playing games of chance or being fascinated by stories where luck seemed to impact the outcome. On the other hand, while he has some Physical Psychic

talent, he'll never be as adept or as dynamic as a *Physical Psychic P.C.C.* It should also be noted that the focus of his psychic abilities from his scientific point of view also limits the selection of Physical Psionic abilities available to him.

Special Lucky Psychic P.C.C. Abilities:

1. "Lucky Dice": The character is inexplicably able to alter the *Chaotic Dynamics* of his surroundings in his favor. This talent potentially enables the psychic to successfully pull off skills, combat maneuvers, saving throws and other "chance" related outcomes when the odds are against him. This is one of the abilities that make him seem "lucky" to other people.

When making a skill check or other roll that requires percentile dice: The player rolls two ten-sided dice as normal, but he chooses which die he wants to be the "tens die" and the "ones die" **AFTER** they have been rolled. Example: Eddie is attempting a "Gambling (Dirty Tricks)" skill roll and needs to roll a 40% or lower with the percentile dice to be a success. Instead of calling which colors are representing tens or ones before rolling, Eddie declares that he's using this ability and then rolls the dice. Let's say that the numbers rolled on the dice were an "8" and a "2." Eddie decides that the "2" will be the tens die and the "8" will be the ones die, resulting in a successful 28% skill roll!

Note: While this ability can help beat the odds of a situation, a poor die roll can still occur and effectively void this ability. If Eddie had rolled a "4" and a "5," neither a 45% nor a 54% would have succeeded.

When making a combat roll, saving throw or other action that requires a twenty-sided die: The player may roll two twenty-sided dice and choose the roll he likes the best. Similar to what was mentioned above, there is no guarantee of a successful outcome, as both dice could roll low numbers. In cases like this, the unsuccessful action is "just meant to be," or he's having a moment of plain bad luck, something even a Lucky Psychic encounters sometimes.

Duration: Instant, but must be declared before the roll is made. Considered to be part of the same action as this ability.
I.S.P.: 5

2. "Crap Shoot": The Lucky Psychic can attempt to force his luck-altering talents upon his enemies to increase the chances of their failing to perform a particular action. However, his lack of control creates very unpredictable outcomes, and sometimes the bad luck affects him or his allies instead of his target.

A successful roll could potentially alter the effectiveness of (if not outright sabotage) their target's skill attempts like Singing, Performance, Dance, Cryptography, Pick Locks, and other skills as much as it could cause them to err in all sorts of physical challenges, like throwing a poor punch during a boxing match, slipping up during a gymnastics feat, poorly aim during a dart throwing contest, and more.

The player selects an opponent/target and rolls 2D6. The number rolled determines the following effects:

Rolled 2 ("Snake Eyes"): While nothing happens to the target, the Lucky Psychic inexplicably loses 12 I.S.P. (including the original 6 needed to activate this power), or goes down to 0 I.S.P. if fewer than 12 points remain. The psychic's lost I.S.P. returns over time as normal. Furthermore, the next *player character* or ally of the Lucky Psychic who performs an action (combat, saving throw or skill) suffers a -30% to his skill/percentage roll or a -6 to his combat/saving throw action!

Rolled 3 ("Crap Out"): Nothing happens to the target, but the psychic still loses the 6 I.S.P. spent on this ability.

Rolled 4: The target suffers a -5% penalty to his next percentile roll or -1 to his next combat roll or saving throw, whichever roll comes first.

Rolled 5: The target suffers a -10% penalty to his next percentile roll or a -2 to his next combat roll or saving throw, whichever roll comes first.

Rolled 6: The target suffers a -15% penalty to his next percentile roll or a -3 to his next combat roll or saving throw, whichever roll comes first.

Rolled 7 or 11: The target will automatically fail his next dice roll attempt, whether it is for a skill (treat it as if he rolled a 100%), a combat roll or a saving throw (treated as if a Natural 1 was rolled). In addition, the player does not spend the 6 I.S.P. cost; in fact he inexplicably gains 12 I.S.P.! The 12 I.S.P. is added to the character's I.S.P. total, even if it's more than the character's maximum amount. These extra I.S.P. will be available for one round per level of experience before they dissipate. Even better, if the psychic rolls a "7 or 11" during an encounter with a supernatural or magical threat, he does not spend the 6 I.S.P. for this ability; instead he gains 24 I.S.P. points! However, once the supernatural or magic threat is gone, the character loses the additional 24 I.S.P.

Rolled 8: The target suffers a -20% penalty to his next percentile roll or a -4 to his next combat roll or saving throw, whichever roll comes first.

Rolled 9: The target suffers a -25% penalty to his next percentile roll or a -5 to his next combat roll or saving throw, whichever roll comes first.

Rolled 10: The target suffers a -30% penalty to his next percentile roll or a -6 to his next combat roll/saving throw, whichever roll comes first.

Rolled 12 ("Boxcars"): Nothing happens to the target, but the player's remaining I.S.P. is somehow blocked (or "boxed-up") and will not be available for about the next six to twelve seconds (the next 1D4+1 actions). The Lucky Psychic still spends the 6 I.S.P. for using this talent. Once the time is up, his remaining I.S.P. will become available again with no other side effects.

Range: 20 feet (6.1 m), +2 feet (0.6 m) per level of experience; line of sight.

Duration: Instant, counts as one action. This talent must be declared before the target of this ability attempts the skill/action the Lucky Psychic wants to alter.

I.S.P.: 6

3. "Tough Luck": When an opponent rolls a "Natural 1" while attacking the Lucky Psychic, the player rolls percentile dice to determine the extent of his opponent's *tough luck*:

01-30%: The opponent was somehow distracted or was tripped up or stumbled while performing the attack, which resulted in a complete miss. Furthermore, the opponent is off balance or "thrown off his game"; his next immediate combat action roll (strike, parry, dodge, etc.) is at a -2 penalty.

31-50%: The opponent's stumble or trip was more severe and he falls down, losing one action and the initiative.

51-70%: The opponent's physical weapon is lost or broken. If it's a gun, it will jam and needs to be fixed before being operable

again. If it's a melee weapon, it slipped free of the opponent's hand while striking and flies at least ten feet (3 m) away, and must be retrieved to use it again. If magic, psionics, claws or some other type of weapon was used that doesn't apply here, roll again.

71-80%: Opponent accidentally hits a nearby ally of his for half the damage. If there's no ally nearby, then the opponent was somehow distracted or was tripped up or stumbled while performing the attack, which resulted in a complete miss. Furthermore, the opponent is off balance or "thrown off his game"; his next immediate combat action roll (strike, parry or dodge, etc.) is at a -2 penalty.

81-90%: Opponent accidentally hits a nearby ally of his for full damage. If there's no ally nearby, then the opponent's stumble or trip was more severe and he falls down, losing one action and the initiative.

91-100%: Opponent accidentally hits a nearby ally of his for double damage! If there's no ally nearby, then the opponent's physical weapon is lost or broken. If it's a gun, it will jam and needs to be fixed before being operable again. If it's a melee weapon, it slipped free of the opponent's hand and flies at least ten feet (3 m) away, and must be retrieved to use it again. If neither of the above options is applicable, the G.M. has free rein to come up with something embarrassing and debilitating to the opponent that best fits the situation.

Note to G.M.s: Do get creative with the situations and circumstances of the opponent's blunders and feel free to add any additional penalties that might apply. Simply saying "he tripped" or "he missed you somehow" all the time takes the fun and creative potential out of this ability. Keep in mind that the psychic does not need the appropriate psychic ability to create an outcome. As long as the action and/or outcome is explainable through one of the *Physical Psionic* abilities (starting on page 107 of **Beyond the Supernatural™, 2nd Edition**), go with it.

Duration: Instant and does not cost the psychic an action.
I.S.P. Cost: None.

4. "Lucky Break": This is a simple but effective ability which basically removes an applicable penalty that either the psychic or a nearby ally would have suffered when he made a roll. The character must either see the person he is applying this ability to or must somehow be involved in what the person is doing. (Example: The Lucky Psychic is riding in the same car his target is driving and negates the applicable penalty for driving around a corner extremely fast while in the rain.) This ability can be used to negate penalties for skill rolls, combat rolls or saving throws. The player must declare he is using this ability before the roll is made. Note that while this can negate a penalty for that particular action or skill roll, any continuing penalties or future penalties will stand unless the Lucky Psychic uses this ability again.

Distance: Self or up to 10 feet (3 m) + 1 foot (0.3 m) per level.

Duration: Instant and does not cost the psychic an action.
I.S.P. Cost: 2

5. "Butterfly Effect": The Lucky Psychic can inexplicably (and subconsciously) use a variety of *Physical Psionic* traits to create minor changes in his surrounding environment. Even more impressive is that he can consciously alter, delay, halt or create the small difference that yields a diverging outcome and changes the physical outcome of a situation. He could improve the odds of flipping a coin to the side he wants, improve his odds of winning when playing confidence games (or alternatively improve the odds of tricking his opponent), or successfully perform small feats involving probability (like rolling dice or drawing the winning *lucky duck* from a tub of water). He could even trigger freak occurrences like pipes bursting, electrical appliances failing, light bulbs suddenly going out, a shower suddenly changing from hot to cold water, a doorknob coming out of the door when pulled, and many other subtle, random occurrences. This ability also provides him with moments of dumb luck when trying to perform skills he doesn't have and making lucky guesses about areas of knowledge he doesn't possess.

When altering a specific item or creating a specific event in the environment: Add the character's I.Q. and M.E. attributes together and add +5 per level to this total. Use the sum as the percentage chance to successfully create an outcome in his favor. The character may also perform the Lucky Dice ability described above in conjunction with this ability to improve his odds of success.

Note: The psychic can only directly declare the action and outcome of an effect of something which he can touch and which can be performed subtly, like flipping a coin to the side he wants, playing confidence games, throwing a dart at the bull's-eye of a dartboard multiple times (hat trick), throwing a basketball from halfway down the court and getting "nuthin' but net," performing card tricks or other sleight of hand tricks, and the like. The effects cannot appear to be supernatural in nature; they must be scientifically logical and explainable. Which means the psychic cannot throw a football or a dart beyond his physical limits, but what he can throw looks spectacular and precise.

When altering the potential outcome of a situation beyond the psychic's reach, the player is allowed to declare his intended outcome or goal. However, as the ability is performed subconsciously by the psychic, the player has no say in exactly what was altered/affected to create the outcome or goal he wanted; it's always the G.M.'s call.

Range: All changes must take place within 20 feet (6.1 m) +2 feet (0.3 m) per level of experience (something beyond this range cannot be involved in the effect).

Trying to *dumb luck* perform a skill the psychic does not have: Add the character's I.Q. and P.P. attributes together and add +5 per level to the total. Use the sum as the percentage chance to successfully perform the skill. The character may also perform the "Lucky Dice" ability in conjunction with this ability to improve his odds of success. The character must have all of the necessary items/equipment to perform skills like *Cooking, Brewing, First Aid, Demolitions, Mechanical skills*, and so on. And a successful roll will only give a serviceable outcome; it will never be of professional quality. **Note:** Failing to perform a skill the psychic does not have could have dramatic and drastic consequences. Imagine trying to perform emergency surgery without the proper skills for it; the psychic could get extremely lucky and save the patient's life, but failing the skill attempt will probably kill the patient and therefore should only be attempted as a last resort.

Trying to perform a *lucky guess* with an intellectual skill the psychic does not have: Take the character's I.Q. attribute and add +5 per level for the total. Use the sum as the percentage chance to successfully perform the lucky guess. The character may also perform the "Lucky Dice" ability in conjunction with this ability to improve his odds of success. The character may add 10% to the total if he has a skill that's related to the one he's trying to perform. (Example: Eddie has the *Streetwise* skill and tries to lucky guess the correct answer or response of a *Streetwise: Weird* related question.)

Note: The character will only correctly guess the answer to that particular question. A new question means a new lucky guess is required.

Limitations: While Butterfly Effect is more open to interpretation than others, the effects have to be small, subtle and within his range of effect. He cannot make a potted plant fall from a balcony onto someone head if it's too high for this talent to reach. A successful outcome must always be something that benefitted the Lucky Psychic directly; his allies may benefit from his lucky outcome, but the outcome's intention has to be in the Lucky Psychic's favor exclusively. This ability can NEVER be performed for the benefit of someone else. For example, Eddie can alter the trajectory of a pair of dice to a favorable number on the craps table whether he rolls them himself or not, but *only* if he has money riding on the roll. He cannot alter someone else's dice roll to a number that's beneficial to only them. He would have to be betting on the roll himself to be able to affect it.

Keep in mind that while the psychic has an impressive mind for mathematics and science and can discern the statistics and probabilities of a given outcome, he still has no idea exactly how or what Physical Psionic abilities were involved in creating the desired effect. And also note that since the psychic is trying to directly manipulate dynamic systems like *chaotic behaviors, strange attractors, quantum physics, quantum mechanics* and other related theories, failing to perform a desired outcome doesn't mean that nothing happens. There are a limitless number of small differences and factors that could take place from his botched attempt at manipulating an event/outcome. Something completely unexpected could still happen and could in fact negatively impact the Lucky Psychic. The G.M. has final say on what actually happened and what the NPCs (if any) will say or do about the event.

Duration: Instant.

I.S.P. Cost: 5

6. Select one of the following additional P.C.C. abilities at levels 2, 4, 6, 8, 11 and 13:

Ambidextrous: Same as the Physical Psychic ability on page 75 of the *Beyond the Supernatural™ RPG, 2ⁿᵈ Ed.*

Extra Fast Runner: Same as the Physical Psychic ability on page 75 of *BTS, 2ⁿᵈ Ed.*

Extra Strong: Same as the Physical Psychic ability on page 76 of *BTS, 2ⁿᵈ Ed.*

Extra Tough: Same as the Physical Psychic ability on page 76 of *BTS, 2ⁿᵈ Ed.*

Iron Constitution: Same as the Physical Psychic ability on page 76 of *BTS, 2ⁿᵈ Ed.*

Quick Reflexes: Same as the Physical Psychic ability on page 76 of *BTS, 2ⁿᵈ Ed.*

Meditation: Same as the Healing Psionic on page 101 of *BTS, 2ⁿᵈ Ed.*

Remember Numbers: This skill is the ability to picture and remember numbers instantly and permanently. This includes phone numbers, addresses, and combination lock sequences and so on. This variation on the Total Recall ability is restricted exclusively to numbers. **Base Skill:** 76% +4% per level of experience. A failed roll means the number is forgotten.

Exceptional Mathematics: This skill provides the natural ability to automatically understand and perform advanced mathematics in one's mind with the accuracy and speed of a calculating machine. This includes simple addition, subtraction, multiplication, division, fractions, percentages, algebra, geometry, calculus and so on. **Base Skill:** 80% +4% per level of experience. A failed roll means the attempted mathematical calculation was incorrect.

Select one of the following Physical Psionic abilities: Alter Aura, Deaden Senses, Death Trance, Ectoplasm, Electrokinesis, Hydrokinesis, Impervious to Fire, Impervious to Poison/Toxin, Leidenfrost Effect, Levitation, Nightvision, Resist Pain, Telekinesis, Telekinetic Leap, Telekinetic Lift, Telekinetic Punch or Telekinetic Push.

Note: The Lucky Psychic lacks the focus to learn some of the more attentive abilities, like *Advanced Meditation* or *Restorative Trance*.

Lucky Psychic P.C.C.

Also known as: Synchroniciteer, Probability Master and Lucky $#*+!

Attributes: Standard 3D6 determination; see Character Creation in the rules section of the *Beyond the Supernatural™ RPG, 2nd Ed.*

Attribute Bonuses: +1D4 to I.Q., M.E. and P.B. or +1D4 to P.S., P.P. and P.E.

Alignment: Any, but the majority of characters tend to be one of the selfish alignments (due to the nature of the beast in this case). Characters of good alignments will be hard-pressed to use their lucky talents to lie, cheat and steal and other less savory uses of their abilities.

P.C.C. Bonuses (in addition to possible attribute bonuses): Needs a 12 or higher to save vs psychic attacks, add +30% to any two occupational Science skills the character has, and add +10% to the remaining Occupational, Elective or Secondary Science skills. Select two additional Elective Skills & Secondary Skills (+10%), +1 to Perception Rolls and add +1 at levels 2, 4, 7, 11 and 13, +2 to save vs Horror Factor, +1 save vs Possession and Disease, +2 save vs hypnosis, mind control and illusions, and +1 to save vs Telepathic and Empathic probes and attacks.

P.C.C. Limitations and Penalties: Closed to the Supernatural. Although the Lucky Psychic possesses psi-powers, he is not receptive to the subtle sensations or emanations of the supernatural or the paranormal. He is simply not "tuned in" to the psychic vibrations and cannot see the invisible, see auras, ghosts or magical radiation. However, his enemies may be able to sense him.

Being closed to the supernatural is not all bad. It means his scientific and physical focus and closed psyche shield the character from supernatural forces, providing a natural defense to possession, magic and psychic attacks (see P.C.C. Bonuses mentioned previously). This natural resistance coupled with the character's own psi-abilities can make him a dangerous opponent to supernatural creatures. Ironically, this defense also makes the character vulnerable, because he lacks the ability to see or sense the presence of his inhuman foes until they take a visible form or he is guided by a Psychic Sensitive, making teamwork essential.

Unless stated otherwise, each psychic attack or use of a psionic ability counts as one of the character's melee attacks or actions.

P.P.E. (Potential Psychic Energy) Points: Roll 1D6; most of the character's P.P.E. has been spent on his aptitude of science and his unique psychic abilities.

I.S.P. (Psychic Inner Strength) Points: 2D4, +2 per level of experience. (x2, x4, x6, x8) The details concerning I.S.P. use are the same as the Physical Psychic ability on page 76 of *BTS, 2nd Ed.*

Recovering I.S.P.: Similar to the Physical Psychic ability on page 76 of *BTS, 2nd Ed.* However, this psychic is not as adept at mind over matter as a dedicated Physical Psychic and does not get the Meditation ability automatically (must be selected).

Selecting Physical Psychic Abilities: Psi-powers for this character include the Special P.C.C. Abilities listed previously, plus a small selection of Physical Psionic abilities. Select 1D4 Physical Psionic abilities at level one. Any further abilities must be selected via the P.C.C. abilities above (#6).

Occupation: The Lucky Psychic's choice of occupation usually depends on which aspect of his talents he appreciates the most. The more intellectual types would find a medical, scientific or engineering occupation to be most appealing (even if their interest is in the academia of these fields). They might also enjoy detective, forensic, CSI or anthropology work or even psychic investigating.

In an odd twist, the intellectual Lucky Psychic might even find Skeptic/Debunking work an interesting challenge (specializing in using his scientific knowledge to debunk hoaxes). While he may be hesitant to debunk psychic abilities (being psychic himself), his logical mind backed by an aptitude for science and mathematics can still pick out the flaws and hoaxes of so-called "miracles" and "paranormal phenomena" almost as well as a Nega-Psychic (use the "Skeptic's Viewpoint" on page 61 of *BTS, 2nd Edition* for examples of plausible explanations). **Note:** Ironically, a Lucky Psychic will dislike working with Nega-Psychic debunkers as their "Psychic Disruptor" talents dampen his abilities the same as other psychics.

The more action-oriented Lucky Psychics would probably be into physical occupations, especially ones where they can benefit from (and show off) their lucky talents the most, such as athletic competitions, high stakes gambling, entertaining and stage magic. But other avenues, like criminal occupations (especially con artistry), espionage agent, bounty hunting, police work, firefighting or even professional driving (especially racing) have potential to the Lucky Psychic who likes to live fast and dangerous.

Common Skills: All.

Standard P.C.C. Equipment: Depends on the orientation of the Lucky Psychic. Those who consider themselves "intellectual" minded will use the "Genius P.C.C." equipment on page 49 of *BTS, 2nd Ed.* Those who consider themselves "physical/action oriented" will use the "Physical Psychic P.C.C." equipment on page 76 of *BTS, 2nd Ed.* Both may be inclined to collect objects that can be used for probability manipulation like dice, coins, a deck of cards or a set of tile games like Dominoes or Mahjong. Many will carry a good luck charm of some sort that they treasure as well.

Housing, Pay and Money in Savings: Treat these notes the same as the standard equipment above. For the "intellectual types" use the "Genius P.C.C." info on 49 of *BTS, 2ⁿᵈ Ed.*, while the "physical/action oriented" types will use the "Physical Psychic P.C.C." info on page 77 of *BTS, 2ⁿᵈ Ed.*

An Example *Lucky Psychic* NPC:

Eddie "Bet da' House" Champman

Born into a family of welfare checks and thievery, Eddie is the byproduct of a broken home in Las Vegas. His mother has always had a thing for danger and dangerous men while at the same time enjoys being lazy and collecting welfare rather than being gainfully employed. His father was a classic crook who spent time in and out of prison constantly and sometimes stayed with his mom when Eddie's stepdad was away in prison.

Not surprisingly, Eddie grew up in the worst neighborhood in Las Vegas. His biological dad is a deadbeat and a waste of time in his life (and his older siblings have since followed in dad's footsteps). Fortunately, his stepdad Harry took an interest in him and took Eddie under his wing (if only to exploit his potential). Harry is a stereotypical pickpocket and hustler, taking advantage of tourists and the naive Las Vegas residents all up and down "the strip" for a living. Seeing the raw talent in Eddie, Harry taught him all he knew about his craft in thievery. As he grew older and wiser, Eddie's criminal methods evolved into hustling and con artistry. As a spoke of his wanderlust personality, Eddie's favored con work was always "quick hustles"; marks that could be taken in a few days tops so he could move on to whatever caught his eye next.

Between his charisma, good looks, natural talent and his budding talents as a Lucky Psychic, Eddie was an instant success as hustler and con artist. Once he was old enough, Eddie fired up his classic Cadillac convertible (he'd just won the pink slip for this sweet ride in a pool table hustle) and has wandered the United States, Mexico and Canada ever since; working cons, hustling and breaking hearts wherever he goes. Occasionally he returns to his old hood and haunts to hang out with his family and friends or break a few laws along "the strip" for old times' sake.

Naturally, Eddie's psychic talents have led him to confronting the supernatural time and time again. But Eddie loves the adrenaline rush and the challenge of dealing with whatever the supernatural throws at him. Eddie keeps a book of all the contacts he meets wherever he goes and has racked up an impressive list of Lazlo Society members and phones ahead whenever he's heading in their direction. If supernatural trouble is brewing, Eddie will make sure to stop by and lend a hand in dealing with it.

While Eddie's not wanted by the authorities at this time (he's not considered "lucky" for nuthin'), there are plenty of people who'd like to get their hands on him. People he's hustled, or conned, or the husbands and fathers of the women he's left behind with broken hearts, and even an organized crime outfit or two would be interested in finding him to get even for past cons. Wherever Eddie goes, trouble follows him on a fast horse.

Note: Eddie's wandering nature means he could show up as an NPC at any random moment during a game adventure. Of course, he might also leave at a moment's notice as well. During the time between his arrival and his departure, he may help the players deal with a supernatural menace, break some lady's heart (or ladies' hearts if given enough time), may get the player characters in hot water with a botched con job, or might even pull off a lucky stunt here or there that saves a player character's life (or the entire party). Eddie lives his life fast and shows no signs of slowing down, and anyone caught up in his whirlwind of activity is bound to find their interactions interesting to say the least.

Character: Edward Champman.

Nickname: Eddie "Bet da' House" Champman.

P.C.C: Lucky Psychic (8ᵗʰ level).

Occupation: Professional con artist, hustler and gambler.

Alignment: Resentfully Unprincipled. He continually tries to be more *Anarchist* or even *Miscreant* minded, but always ends up trying to do the right thing in the end.

Attributes: I.Q. 12, M.E. 13, M.A. 19, P.S. 20, P.P. 18, P.E. 18, P.B. 17, Spd 22.

Skills of Note: Find Contraband 68%, Appraise Antiques 80%, Intelligence 76%, Performance 80%, Seduction 51%, Streetwise 58%, Streetwise Weird 80%, Cardsharp 83%, Gambling 80%, Gambling (Dirty Tricks) 64%, Palming 70%, Concealment 58%, Pick Locks 80%, Pick Pockets 80%, Basic & Advanced Mathematics 98%/98%, Language & Literacy: Spanish 81/85%, Wardrobe & Grooming 88%, Juggling 70%, Running, Body Building & Weight Lifting, W.P. Handguns (+4 to Strike), W.P. Knife (+3 to Strike & Parry and +4 to Throw) and Paired Weapons (provided via *Hand to Hand: Expert* and *Ambidexterity* below).

Hit Points: 57. **S.D.C.:** 49.

Age: 34. **Sex:** Male.

Height: 6 feet, 1 inch (1.8 m). **Weight:** 179 lbs (80.5 kg).

Hair: Jet black, kept short and well groomed. **Eyes:** Brown.

Birth Order: Last born of three.

Money: Eddie's cash on hand is always somewhere from $10 to $100,000 on any given day. Eddie has been known to win big one evening only to lose it all the next on a large bet. One night he's staying in the best room at the Playboy Hotel in Vegas and the next night he's sleeping penniless in his Cadillac. But Eddie's really good at what he does and doesn't worry too much about his cash flow. He's lived on both sides of the poverty level and knows how to survive (and excel) on both sides.

General Appearance: Eddie is a tall and toned Caucasian male with a medium build in his early thirties with dark brown eyes and well kept, raven black hair. His style is almost always boots, jeans (sometimes khakis when he's going someplace fancy) and suspenders strapped over a white 'wife beater' undershirt, topped with a button-up shirt (usually left unbuttoned and favoring the Hawaiian variety). He's also got a fondness for gold necklaces and rings. Eddie's favorite article of clothing is an old trilby he's owned for years, and he is always seen with it either on his head or within his reach.

Disposition: To the uninitiated (and his *marks*), Eddie appears to be a trusting, charming, easy going guy with a fun loving attitude who never takes anything too seriously. Those who know the real Eddie will find him to be a sarcastic, fast talking schemer who's always on the lookout for a sucker. Eddie gets overconfident at times, and loves playing the odds and taking chances he shouldn't. He's old enough to know better, but he's still too young to care.

Family Origin: Of Italian and Slovak ancestry with no known history of psychic phenomena.

Environment: From a low income family in the worst neighborhood of Las Vegas.

Sentiments Towards Mages and Psychics: His experience with them has mostly been positive and he enjoys their company (and their help when dealing with the supernatural). However, he's a little wary of the "sensitive types," as he marked a Psychic Sensitive once. The psychic called him out on his "mark" when Eddie tried to sell him a fake antique (discovered via *Empathy, Thought-Reading* and *Object Reading*) for far more than it was worth. Eddie has since been more careful about choosing his marks.

Sentiments Towards Non-Humans: Eddie can't help but find the paranormal and the supernatural as interesting as he does terrifying. His puckish and playful side comes out when he gets an "adrenaline rush" from the presence of the supernatural and he loves to cause mishaps and misfortune to befall the vile creatures while the "big guns" in his party do more of the actual fighting. He's no coward, however, and will go toe to toe with the supernatural when needed, he just enjoys his lucky talents and finds his opponents' floundering and fuddling to be hilarious.

Goals in Life: Eddie really hasn't bothered to settle down as of yet, as he enjoys being a "fly by night operator" who flies by the seat of his pants. So at this point in time he's content with continuing his con work, winning as much as he can (and while he can), and showing off as he wanders from place to place.

Insanity: Eddie once picked up a Succubus in a singles bar one night, oblivious to the fact she was playing him as much as he was playing her. She unveiled her true self in a seedy hotel room she'd taken him to, and Eddie's fast thinking and lucky talents were all that allowed him to escape her trap. Eddie now nurses a paranoia of monsters in female bodies ever since (working its way to a phobia), and always carries a hidden silver-plated dagger on his person when he goes out prowling for women; ya know, just in case. Also has a "psycho-reliance" on an object (see special equipment).

Reason for Paranormal Investigation: Eddie's work and wanderings eventually led him to a chance meeting with psychics and the supernatural. Eddie enjoys the adrenaline surges of combating the supernatural as much as he does the company of other psychics. He's in it more for the thrill than anything else.

Outlook on Being Psychic: Eddie feels blessed about being a psychic, especially the "lucky" kind. Feels like he was born to do what he does and enjoys it to the max. While he's not religious nor has he ever made any vows to use his powers for good, he always ends up doing good deeds with his talents when it counts the most (and in spite of himself for doing so).

P.P.E.: 2. **I.S.P.:** 20.

Psionics: In addition to his talents as a Lucky Psychic (described above), Eddie has the following abilities and Psionics: Ambidexterity (provides W.P. Paired Weapons), Extra Tough (a lot tougher than he looks), Remember Numbers 84%, Quick Reflexes (also a lot faster than he looks), Levitation, Telekinesis, Telekinetic Push and Resist Pain.

Hand to Hand Skill: Expert (part street schooled, part self defense classes, all quick & scrappy).

Attacks per Melee: 5

Bonuses of Note: +4 to Perception Rolls, +4 to Initiative, +5 to Strike, Parry and Dodge, +3 to Pull Punch, +2 to Roll with punch, +2 to Disarm, Critical Strike on a Natural 18-20, +5 damage on all physical attacks, Kick Attack does 1D8 damage, Karate Kick does 2D6 damage, Karate Punch does 2D4 damage, Backhand Strike does 1D4 damage, Body Flip/Throw does 1D6 damage & victim loses initiative. 55% to Invoke Trust, 35% bonus to Charm, +2 to save save magic/poison and +2 to save vs Horror Factor.

Housing: Eddie owns a nice house in an upscale part of Las Vegas, which he won via a high stakes bout of gambling several years ago. That being said, Eddie is always wandering or traveling and is never home. A few years ago he invited his family to move into the house to "keep an eye on it" for him while he's away. In reality, he'd caught wind of how dangerous his old hood's become and even though he still doesn't really like any of them, they are still family and he wanted them to live in a safer place and asked them to move in. His family greedily accepted and has made themselves at (his) home.

Equipment: Eddie is always traveling (or in some cases, fleeing) from place to place and never carries more than what he can fit into his Cadillac. This means he'll usually only have his clothing, travel bag (soaps, shampoo, cologne and other personal items), con artist materials (forged IDs, confidence game items, expensive looking antique items or good knock-offs of original items of value, etc.). His most important item to his work is a well maintained black book which contains a variety of contacts, including ID forgers, counterfeiters, shills and other con artists located in a variety of cities and towns and how to contact or locate them.

Eddie's personal pride and joy is a light blue, vintage, 1969 Cadillac convertible he won in a high stakes game of pool (Eddie hustled his butt off to win it, of course). Eddie keeps his prized car well maintained (keeps a list of good mechanics in his black book) and always in a presentable, ready shape for the occasional car show.

Special Equipment: "One Legged Blackie" is Eddie's lucky black rabbit's foot. Eddie has owned *Blackie* since his first successful con job he performed back in high school. While it has no inherent powers of its own, Eddie has developed a psycho-reliance on *Blackie* over the years and always kisses "her" before he starts a con or goes into a high stakes gam- bling or dangerous situation. If it is ever lost, Eddie will suffer from the "psycho-reliance" penalties (found on page 154 of *BTS, 2ⁿᵈ Ed.*) until either *Blackie* is recovered or he finds a new lucky object.

Two Favorite Quotes: When asked if one should place a bet on a particular game or situation, his responses are almost always either, *"Bet da' House,"* or *"Eh, stay away from that one."*

Dark Day Chronicles, Vol. I

A Nightbane® Short Story

By Jeremy Hutchins

On the morning of March 6ᵗʰ, 2000, I knew the world would never be the same again. Being a night owl, I was rarely in bed before daybreak, so when I glanced at the clock at 6:10 that morning, I knew something was not right. Normally the windows of my home were alight with predawn luminescence, but that day it was still pitch black. Intrigued, I walked over and stared out at Baker Street, which passed right in front of my suburban home. The street lights were off and traffic was very light, which was normal for that time, but the sky is what caught my attention. Not only was there no sign of the moon, which I had been staring at barely three hours before, but I couldn't see a single star! It was like a funeral shroud pulled over the world, blinding us.

Creepy as it was, if that had been the culmination of the strangeness, I wouldn't have worried. My mind was already formulating ideas of what could cause such an event. Terribly thick storm clouds, an unexpected eclipse, my clock was wrong... there could be a thousand reasons why the night sky was suddenly so strange. It wasn't until I began to feel something within, an incessant tug, an irresistible urge, that I truly began to worry. My body seemed to be acting of its own accord, but in a way familiar to me. Regardless of the familiarity, it still scared the hell out of me. Never before had my body forced the change on me like this!

Sorry, I get ahead of myself. Let me start from the beginning. My name is Trystan Arthur Dey, and I'm a Nightbane. Unless you're one of the few in the "know," that means little, so let me explain. Nightbane look human, but we're not. We are shapeshifters, able to take a second, more powerful form we call a Morphus. No two Nightbane in their Morphus forms look alike. There are dozens of theories why, but the one I subscribe to most is that our Morphus is a reflection of our true selves. It's our essence, our soul made flesh and laid bare for all to see. For some odd reason, most Morphus forms are hideous to behold, but not all. Some, frequently referred to as "Kens" or "Barbies," are beautiful, but they are the rare minority of my kind. Maybe we, as a race, are a violent, despicable lot and a hideous Morphus is our punishment for past sins. The violent part seems to have some credence because when we shift, we know on an instinctive level how to cause the most carnage. It's like a baby snake knowing how to kill from birth. It's apparently hardwired into that part of our brain and is triggered when we shift.

Most Nightbane know nothing of their true selves until the first time they change. We call it the Becoming, and it is the single most traumatic experience a Nightbane can possibly have. It starts off with a strange feeling deep within, like an itch you just can't scratch no matter how hard you try. It builds, making you uncomfortable in your own skin. You feel very warm, feverish, and very, very agitated. Nothing seems to help. No drink cools you down, no exercise distracts you, and worst of all, your brain is going a thousand miles a second with the craziest images and feelings you can imagine. I thought I was going insane. Then, like the flip of an unseen switch, your body feels like it literally explodes, revealing a new you beneath. It's you, but it's not. I didn't recognize myself in the mirror; in fact, I scared the crap out of myself to the point where I smashed the mirror and the wall behind it with one swing. I can't begin to describe the sensation of raw power coursing through a Morphus. I felt like I was being electrocuted but it didn't hurt. I'm not ashamed to say that I really, really enjoyed it!

For most, it's absolutely terrifying when it happens. I know of Nightbane who changed and lost their minds in the transformation. It's a lot to assimilate and some can't handle the mental stress. Some killed those around them as they tried to cope with these startling changes and not realizing their newfound strength.

A Morphus form is power incarnate, able to do things reserved only for superheroes in the comics. I'm not the most powerful Nightbane out there, but I can easily flip a car, throw a manhole cover like a Frisbee, run faster than forty miles an hour, and jump high enough to land flat-footed on a two story building's roof. As luck has it, my Morphus has wings, allowing me to fly much faster than I can run. That, too, is addicting.

By the time March 6th arrived, I had just celebrated my 20th birthday. We age, but much slower than humans. I changed my first time when I was 19 so I'm going to be stuck looking 19 for a while. It doesn't sound like such a big deal at first, but knowing I'll look 20 when I'm chronologically a century old takes some getting used to.

Unlike most, I had a mentor who was a Nightbane, so I knew the rules. I knew what to expect and was better able to cope with it than most. He was a friend of my father, who was also a Nightbane. He died before I was born, fighting against something I'll explain another time. My mother died giving birth to me and my sister, which is how I came to live with "Uncle" Julian. He was my parents' best friend and swore to them he would raise us if anything ever happened. Julian helped me to realize what I was at an early age so when my Becoming happened, I was ready. Still shocked the hell out of me, but I coped better than expected.

I mentioned my sister a moment ago. Julian didn't adopt her. Instead she was adopted by a family in Pennsylvania named Murphy. Julian kept tabs on her, but otherwise he didn't tell me until I was older. I was angry at first, to the point I almost had my Becoming at 12, but he managed to calm me down again. He told me that day everything about the Nightbane: who we are, what we do, why we're here, and most especially who our enemies are. Julian didn't think it wise to keep too many of us together in one group. He said it might make for an interesting target, and after hearing about our enemies, I couldn't disagree. One day, I promised myself, I would find my sister and be reunited. One day came on March 6th, which would later be known by the entire world as Dark Day. Oddly enough, I wouldn't be the one to find her. She would find me. This is her tale.

– From the Journal of Trystan Dey

Alarms were annoying devices created by bean-counters to ensure that their work force arrived and left their appointed duty stations at the proper times. As her alarm sounded, it did not announce another dreary day of working an assembly line or some office job from 9 to 5, rather it heralded another day of classrooms and labs at the local Johnstown branch of the University of Pittsburgh. Avalon rolled wearily out of bed without hitting the snooze button – an action that required astounding mental endurance considering it was, after all, Monday morning – and made her way to the bathroom.

As she showered, images of her latest dream floated at the edge of her barely conscious mind. The steaming water might wake most, but she was something of a slow riser, and that recurring dream held most of her thoughts. She leaned forward and put her forehead against the tile wall, allowing the water to flow down her back. The tile was very cool against her face, which felt strangely comforting, and she closed her eyes for a moment to try and recall that image the alarm had disturbed.

The figure haunting her dreams was a man, she was pretty sure, cloaked or hooded and standing in the shadows of some unknown alley. Despite her inability to distinguish features, he felt oddly familiar in a strange way. Some nights he spoke to her and other nights he stood there gesturing, slowly and deliberately. Last night she was pretty sure he spoke, though his words were distant, haunting. While she dreamt of him many times, never before had his presence seemed so... urgent. She strained to remember the words he spoke, but they would not come to her.

"Avalon Lauren Murphy!!"

Avalon nearly jumped out of the shower at the sudden shout, and only then did she realize that she had nearly fallen asleep standing there in the warmth of the shower! It was her mother – adopted mother truthfully, though Avalon never knew another as Mom before her – and she was banging on the door rather loudly.

"You get out of that shower, young lady, before you use all the hot water! I'm cooking breakfast. It should be done by the time you get ready for school."

As quickly as she came, Carolyn Murphy retreated downstairs, giving her daughter a heart attack before doing so thanks to the knocking. Avalon stuck her head out of the shower's curtain and glanced at the clock they had on the wall nearby. She had been in the shower for nearly thirty minutes! By now she was surprised there was hot water still left in the house. Carolyn was after her husband, Tom, to get a larger – not to mention more modern – hot water heater, but he steadfastly refused, citing that age was not always a bad thing. They could take quick showers and baths just as easily as long ones, he maintained. Tom Murphy was a pragmatic man, and being a cop for the past twenty-four years often left him more than a little jaded when it came to trusting people like installers or repairmen in the house. Tom was a dangerous man with his training and a gun, but Carolyn often joked he was far more dangerous to the world with a hammer and saw. He was an excellent policeman with a proven track record, but he certainly was in no danger of upstaging Bob Vila.

Bathing quickly, Avalon dried both herself and her hair, then set off into her room to find suitable clothes for the day when something struck her as odd. She often had strange feelings about impending events in her life – such as when Carolyn fell off a ladder trying to clean out the gutters Tom kept neglecting. Avalon raced home early from high school on her moped and arrived just in time to see it happen and call an ambulance. The doctor congratulated her on the timing - Avalon left out her "vision" of the event, of course - saying that if her mother had lain there for very long, she could have lost enough blood from her injuries to slip into a coma. Avalon felt a similar sensation as that one, though she could "see" nothing. Her previous visions were enough, even if they were slightly ambiguous, to have a general idea of what was happening. Now she had the sensation of danger, but when she closed her eyes all she could see was total darkness. That pitch black caused a shiver to crawl down her spine.

Avalon managed to run a brush through her hair and pull it back when she noticed the windows of her bedroom were somehow off. By now she could usually see the first hints of sunlight peeking through. Instead it was very dark. Pulling on an azure blouse Carolyn recently bought her, Avalon moved to the window and peered out. The street lamps were off, which confused her. They were on timers that shut them off exactly at 7 a.m. every morning. According to her clock it was 7:03 now, but it certainly did not look that way. So why was it still so dark outside? Cars were passing by, though very few given the fact it was Monday morning and most of the city had to be at work that day.

Avalon glanced at the sky again and her brow furrowed. Where were the brighter stars that were always visible, even above the brightness of the small town's lights? This time of the morning the moon was often out of sight and the sun was rising, but since it still looked night she should at least have been able to see some stars. There was nothing. Instead the sky looked like a blanket of the darkest onyx.

She heard her parents call for her downstairs, their tone far beyond concerned. They sounded scared! Avalon rushed downstairs and saw both of her parents sitting on the sofa staring with wide eyes at their television. She could hear some of the broadcast as she entered the room and it caught her attention immediately.

"... no stars or moon, just a solid sheet of total darkness! This is incredible! Astronomers say it is NOT an eclipse."

According to the bottom of the screen, it was a live broadcast from New York City's Channel 3 News Team. The reporter, Dan Witfield according to the caption, was standing on top of a large building and kept staring up into the sky. He was obviously terrified.

The screen changed abruptly as Tom flipped channels to the familiar face of Philly's Channel 12 reporter Zach Wright.

"For those of you just joining us, I want to repeat the events that led to this broadcast. At 6:02 Eastern Standard Time, the east coast of the United States, and possibly the entire country, was plunged into complete darkness. We have unconfirmed reports that the condition exists all over the United States, and calls have even been reported from Canada and Mexico of the same phenomenon. Please stay tuned while we take a station break, and we'll be right back with more coverage of this unique event."

Their telephone rang just as the screen cut to a Diet Dr. Pepper commercial. Tom grabbed the portable unit from its mount beside the sofa. "Murphy here."

It was a short conversation with lots of "yes, sir"s and ending with "I'll be right there, sir." He hung up the phone and turned to his family. "The force is calling in all officers. It's been an hour since this started and we've already got a riot on our hands at the church on Spring Street. Bob says people have been calling non-stop asking if this is the end of the world."

* * *

Pain.

It was unlike any other feeling except, oddly enough, ecstasy. Many times over human history the two were linked together as kindred emotions. Pain creates pleasure and pleasure can sometimes be painful. If that were true, then Gabriel should be the happiest being alive.

He was unlike anything ever seen by humanity. With the same basic build as a human - two arms, two legs, and a head - that was where the similarities ended. His skin and hair were as black as night, causing the being known as Gabriel to look like a man's shadow literally come to life. From his back sprouted ugly, bat-like wings which could bear him aloft, achieving speeds in excess of seventy miles per hour. Each powerful hand ended with wicked, talon like claws that were as horrific as the rest of his terrible form. Around each wrist were snake-like tendrils that appeared to be darkened metal chains nearly ten feet long. They frequently coiled and writhed independently as they flailed of their own accord. They seemed to be part of his being more than any objects of binding.

To anyone he met, Gabriel would appear as a creature from a savage, hellish nightmare. His eyes glowed with a hatred that fed his raw power. To the pain-wracked being he attached himself to, wrapping his tendril-like chains about the man's neck and torso while flashing feral, almost animal teeth in a vicious grin, Gabriel was everything he appeared to be: a nightmare made flesh. Gabriel's people were known as Athanatos, beings touched and blessed with the powers over the five elements (air, earth, fire, water, and death). An Athanatos begins life as a human with a trace of an ancient power within his or her mortal shell. Legend says a race of powerful beings known as the Gregorians, progenitors of the elemental powers, blessed specific human mothers with their gift, allowing their progeny to be born with latent powers. Ofttimes this power was unleashed when the child grew to adulthood, mostly due to stress or danger. Sometimes an Elder Athantos was able to "stoke" the fires within and produce the chance, allowing for a time of reflection and teaching the new Athantos of his abilities. This change, called the Revelation by the Athantos, is the birth from their old life to their new.

Both figures literally hurled from the shadows of an alleyway and onto the sidewalk of a dead-end street as if they were fired from some unseen cannon. Gabriel's "ride" looked human, but in reality he was something far more sinister. Gabriel took no pity on his living taxi. The man served his purpose, giving Gabriel a ride from his prison in the Nightlands back to Earth, and now he would serve one last purpose before suffering a grisly fate that would make even the most sadistic serial killer blanch.

"Fifty-five years, six months, and nine days," the Athanatos - more accurately the Necrosis version of that race whose powers revolved around Death and Decay - hissed into the ear of the Shadow Sorcerer laying beneath him. The Sorcerer was mostly a normal human who was born and raised in the ever-gloom of the Nightlands, resulting in strange "gifts" that allowed him, with great mental and physical effort, to penetrate the potent barrier between the two worlds. Given he was burdened with a very angry Necrosis on his back with powerful tendrils wrapped around his body as he demanded passage back to Earth, it had become quite necessary to risk the trip. The sorcerer lay on the concrete sidewalk, gasping for breath as he remained pinned under Gabriel's surprising weight. Gabriel had been a prisoner in the Nightlands since his capture by one of Hitler's specially-equipped SS occult teams on the Mediterranean island of Sicily in 1945, and the Necrosis had no intentions of going back to that living Hell.

"Y... you... prom... promiss..." the Shadow Sorcerer sputtered as Gabriel's tendrils tightened slowly.

"I promised?" Gabriel growled in his ear, yanking his tendrils roughly. The Sorcerer gagged and his body began to spasm from the unbearable pressure around his neck. "Yes. Yes, I did."

In a very atypical gesture, Gabriel loosened his grip. He stood, allowing the Sorcerer to gasp for much needed oxygen. The Shadow Sorcerer coughed and heaved as he sucked in greedy breaths, but Gabriel ignored him completely. He was home now! After fifty-six years he was back, and there were no words to describe his elation! Rarely in the past half-decade was he left alone more than a few hours. Always the enemy was there, endless minions of the damnable Ba'al, poking and prodding, cutting and gutting, making a living lab rat out of the proud Necrosis warrior. He was a Spartan by birth, a warrior for more than two thousand years, and Gabriel found his confinement and experimentation a humiliation beyond words. And to make matters worse, the Ba'al gained information from him that he never would have given willingly about his people and other supernatural beings on Earth. The Ba'al were powerful inhuman beings with seemingly infinite resources at their disposal – torture, drugs, magic, psionics, and even illusion. They were the undisputed rulers of the terrible Nightlands, and they used all their considerable tools to break the Necrosis. It was an experience that Gabriel would never forget, even if he lived another two millennia, and he would certainly never forgive.

Stepping away from the wheezing Shadow Sorcerer, who finally seemed to be getting his wind back, Gabriel glanced at the night sky and froze in mid-stride. Nothing was there. No stars, no moon... nothing. It looked exactly like the ever-present gloom of the Nightlands' eternally dusky sky. Gabriel spun on the Sorcerer with murder in his eyes and willed his tendrils into motion with but a thought. The unsuspecting Sorcerer had begun to rise as he was suddenly impaled through both shoulders by the wicked spikes on the ends of those deadly appendages. How he shrieked as he was yanked up like a child's toy!

"You lying scum!" Gabriel bellowed. "You said you were taking me to Earth!"

The Shadow Sorcerer nodded emphatically while tears streamed down his dirty face. "I did, m'lord! I did! I swear to you, I did! We are on Earth! I can feel the difference, great one! Can't you?" The man sobbed pitifully as Gabriel shook him violently. His tendrils continued to twist and buckle while in the wounds, ripping wider holes in the Sorcerer's shoulders while his arms and legs flailed in agonized spasms.

Gabriel looked around and saw a few lights in nearby buildings: more than he had ever seen in the dim Nightlands. Continuing to extend his senses, he realized the Sorcerer spoke the truth. With a sudden jerk, Gabriel pulled his tendrils free and let his victim unceremoniously fall on his back. So it started already, he thought. How long had the sky been this way? Had the invasion the Ba'al hinted at for the past few years truly begun?

Gabriel ignored the ruined Sorcerer and turned to start out of the alley when the man, apparently not realizing the Necrosis was leaving, cried out a plea for mercy. Gabriel turned back slowly and gazed at the man like he was some uninteresting object he just discovered. The Shadow Sorcerer managed to get to his knees and bowed profusely, despite his obvious pain.

"Oh please, merciful one! Remember your word and I shall never forget your compassion!"

"I am a man of my word," Gabriel said, and the Sorcerer smiled in sudden relief. "But your sniveling kind deserve to die. Lackeys of the Ba'al, traitors to your own kind, the lot of you are scum."

The Sorcerer shrieked as Gabriel's tendrils pierced his lower abdomen, lifting him easily from the dirty concrete. He tried to scream as Gabriel, face still as passive as if he were playing Solitaire, entwined those lethal appendages about the man's spine, but the pain was too intense. No sound emerged as he writhed on the end of those snake-like extensions of Gabriel's will. With a sharp tug, flesh ripped and blood splattered everything for a dozen feet as the Shadow Sorcerer was literally torn in two! That was a sound one never forgot, and Gabriel savored it like a masterful symphony. Each half was thrown to opposite sides of the alley as Gabriel reveled in the carnage. His only wish was that he could gift-wrap the halves and send them back to the Ba'al as a final farewell.

Powerful wings snapped once and bore him aloft. Gabriel was out of sight within seconds, leaving in his wake a scene that would terrify any who found the sickening remains. Even now no thought was given to his actions. Gabriel's sole intent was to survey the area and learn exactly where he had appeared on Earth. As he reached a perfect height for both gliding and reconnaissance, he extended his senses and enjoyed the feeling of freedom.

* * *

Tom was gone for barely an hour when the television began broadcasting local coverage of the trouble on the streets of Johnstown. Things were getting crazier out there by the minute and more than once Carolyn and Avalon heard the sounds of gunfire a little too close to their home. The doors and windows were locked and bolted while Tom's spare gun, a .38, sat nearby, fully loaded. Mother and daughter leaned on one another for support as the minutes ticked by, hoping for their phone to ring with good news that this madness was ending.

The media was calling it the Apocalypse and religions around the world were, for once, in full agreement. It did not take long for news to come in that this was a world-wide event, not just centralized in their particular area. Reports of riots in every major city were televised and stories that would have never been broadcast on news stations were now being told with complete certainty.

Monsters roamed the streets.

At first the news anchors were careful to explain away sightings as mass hysteria, but after one particularly unsettling video shot by Channel 12's own cameraman, Henry Davis, was aired, the debate was put to rest. Most reports were from people obviously distraught and unreliable, but Davis was a cameraman for 25 years and covered stories in the Persian Gulf, Grenada, Iran, Iraq, and Beirut. He was as calm under fire and duress as any combat veteran. Henry's video clearly showed something hairy, large, and growling madly as it prowled down a city street in the direct path of car lights. It was ripping up street signs with its bare hands and hurling them incredible distances! No one knew what it was, and the only person who dared to approach it had been grabbed and tossed away like one of the signs! Militia nuts in the area opened fire on the thing and reportedly killed it, but no signs of a body were found - only blood.

More images of flying things and something that resembled a church gargoyle were shown, but every bit of footage besides that of Davis was far too grainy and distant to see much. Two hours into the chaos and the hospitals and clinics in Johnstown were filled to capacity. More warnings were issued for people to stay in their homes and not leave under ANY circumstances while anarchy reigned in the streets.

Carolyn spoke quietly to Avalon as they watched the horror, always trying to smile and act as if things were not as bad as they appeared. Regardless of how she made it all sound, Avalon wasn't fooled. Things were very, very bad at the moment, and they were getting worse.

Avalon tensed an hour later as she felt a familiar, strange sensation. It was a prelude to one of her visions, but again she saw nothing. No hint, no prelude of what might be coming. All she could see was a complete, pervasive darkness. A noise like that of a shotgun blast brought both of the women to their feet as their back door was completely splintered with impossible force!

Standing where she was, Avalon had a direct line of sight to what was left of the door, and the young woman's heart skipped a beat at the sight of what was framed within that gaping hole.

The figure resembled a proverbial black knight, dressed from head to toe in a kind of onyx armor. At well over six feet in height, it looked almost skeletal despite the plating which covered it entirely. The face - or was it a helmet? - appeared to be skeletal in design as well, with glowing, brilliant eyes and a death's head grin on its immobile visage. One armored hand held a formidable weapon which resembled a long staff with axe heads on either end. At the crest of each axe head was set a short protrusion that looked very much like a spear's head! Like the armor of the being, the weapon was completely black. What looked like a horse's tail plume emerged from the top of the helmet and rolled down over one armored shoulder. It moved its head from side to side as if studying the room. Avalon heard what sounded like a guttural growl that could not have possibly come from anything remotely human as it strode into the kitchen and cleaved the table in half with a lazy swing from that hideous axe!

Carolyn screamed as she stared wide-eyed in the kitchen. Both women were frozen in place, one in paralyzing fear and the other in pure horror. As the creature's head whipped to face the sudden shriek, Carolyn violently shoved Avalon towards the front door.

"RUN!" Carolyn screamed as she turned her attention back to their armored intruder.

Avalon could barely grasp what was happening when she heard the deafening gunshots erupt from the .38 her mother produced. Each shot made her jump almost out of her skin! Above the din of gunfire and through ringing ears, Avalon heard the armored being issue a piercing screech that sounded like a Velociraptor from the Jurassic Park movies. In slow motion, she watched Carolyn fire the last bullet as the armored being burst into the room with impossible speed! It charged Carolyn with spear-axe leveled and Avalon knew in that instant there was nothing she could do to change the inevitable. She could only reach helplessly for Carolyn and scream as the spear made contact with and then lifted her mother! The spear head drove through her soft flesh with terrible ease and the thing kept driving forward until it literally pinned the impaled woman to the wall. Carolyn's feet kicked in agonizing pain as her pale face turned to regard Avalon one last time. The .38 dropped with a thud on the hardwood floor as she fell forward on the weapon's haft, dying hands clutching the deadly weapon futilely. The murderer threw back its head and issued another of those terrifying shrieks. Avalon's heart skipped a beat when she heard an answering call from outside!

* * *

Gabriel flew for at least two hours, gliding as much as he was able to conserve energy. He was still quite weak from his long captivity and he knew how much flying could, and would, tax him. He altered his height based on his needs, but he always remained low enough to take advantage of his extraordinary senses.

Before his capture in 1945, Gabriel had encountered perhaps two or three other supernatural beings every decade. It was a fairly reliable estimate over his long lifetime and something he had come to rely upon. This did not include his fellow Athanatos, whom he met with regularly enough over the centuries; only the other races of supernatural beings. As he soared over small and large towns alike, his senses were now abuzz with hits of supernatural beings of all kinds. It seemed the world was veritably teeming with them now compared to just before his capture, and it was impossible to say if they were friendly, indifferent, or hostile. Sometimes he felt what were called Nightbane, and twice he sensed the diminutive creatures his people had come to call Guardians. Most often, though, he saw more than felt the minions of the Nightlords: Hounds, Hunters, Doppelgangers, Hollow Men, and even a few Hound Masters!

Gabriel wanted to take the fight to the enemy, but thus far every group he encountered was in numbers beyond even his considerable skill. Hounds, the foot soldiers of the Ba'al, were certainly no easy target. Gabriel could take one in an even fight, maybe even two at once. However, once the numbers moved to three-to-one odds, things were an entirely different story. Gabriel had never seen even the most battle-hardened veteran among his own people defeat more than five Hounds at once. Gabriel's mentor was the one who performed that particular feat and Gabriel could only gape at the powerful being's prowess in that battle. The fight nearly killed his mentor in the process, but he healed quickly once it was over. Another gift all Athanatos shared – superior healing.

He knew from road signs he could read far below that he was in Pennsylvania. Seeing a small town not too far away, Gabriel decided to find a safe place to rest there for a while before continuing along. As he flew into the town and over some residences, though, something caught his sharp eyes.

A squad of four Hounds was on the move, running sometimes on their feet like men and other times on all fours like animals. They were remarkable creatures, Gabriel had to admit: fast, incredibly strong, tough, and without any hint of mercy or pity in their evil bodies. In all, they were perfect foot soldiers for the amoral, alien Nightlords. Gabriel surmised they had a purpose based on their movements, and this wasn't some random scouting party. They never dallied or investigated their surroundings, instead they stopped only to get their bearings and sniff about before heading off again. On instinct, Gabriel gave chase high enough to escape their uncanny senses.

Ten minutes later he saw their destination and wondered to himself what brought them to this particular home. Two of them hid in the shadows in the front of the house while the other two moved around back. With an ear-splitting sound of smashed timber, one proceeded to storm in through the back door while the other moved in a little more carefully behind it. As Gabriel drifted lower, he could now sense the reason for their actions. There was a Nightbane inside.

* * *

Rage the likes of which Avalon had never felt coursed through her frame. A gymnast almost from birth, she was thin but with lean muscles wrought from years of practice. Avalon could perform feats of agility and strength most women her age would never consider attempting. She knew in the back of her mind that despite her strength, this creature, whatever it was, would in no way be threatened by her. Something else triggered in her mind, however, and washed away the fear like rain. Her anger outweighed her common sense and some nagging sensation was urging her to simply let go.

And she did exactly that.

The howling creature seemed to remember something and spun on her a few seconds later. Its hidden face was unreadable, of course, a still mask that never moved, yet she seemed to get a hint of surprise from it. The deadly weapon used to kill her mother was yanked violently from the wall and Carolyn's corpse fell to the floor. The creature regarded Avalon for a moment as it brought its weapon up threateningly while issuing a low, dangerous hiss.

Avalon didn't care about the danger this thing represented. Fire coursed through her veins and she was drunk on this newfound power! She felt like she could rip this monster in half with minimal effort. For some reason, the being before her seemed to be a little shorter and far less threatening than it did a moment before. Already her calculating mind was formulating the best attack strategies, somehow instinctively knowing likely weak spots and guesstimating its speed and strength. It all happened within a span of a few heartbeats.

* * *

Gabriel circled high enough to avoid detection from the Hounds and watched their movements. He heard screaming and gunfire from the house and knew time was short. When one of the Hounds in the shadows moved onto the front porch for a better look, Gabriel dove with all of his considerable speed towards it. The Hounds began whooping and shrieking in those excited warbles of theirs, which meant they sensed him. Luckily for Gabriel, the stupid things were cunning, but not very bright, so neither of them even bothered to look up.

Gabriel ignored the cool wind against his face in favor of venting some of his insatiable rage on the enemy he loathed. The Hound standing before the front door was his target and it noticed the diving Necrosis a millisecond too late. Tendrils dove between chinks in the Hound's armor as talon-like claws thrust into its armored face. Gabriel pulled out of his dive exactly as he made contact with the Hound and it howled indignantly as it was taken off its feet and made into an impressive wrecking ball.

Gabriel and the Hound barreled through the door with a deafening crack and hurled into the living room in a blur of shapes. Gabriel's clawed hands were buried enough in the Hound's helmet to keep hold while his feet were perched on the Hound's thighs. He rode the vicious creature into the room like a living surfboard. His tendrils wrapped around the Hound's shoulders and arms like twin snakes, keeping it from fighting back as they slammed into the empty sofa, destroying it in the process. The crippled Hound howled in agony while Gabriel loosed an unearthly cry of his own.

* * *

Avalon and her foe dropped into crouches and were circling when the Hound stiffened and jerked its head towards the front door. Before she could take advantage of the distraction, the door literally exploded inward and two more nightmares spilled into her life. The first looked identical to the one she now faced while the other, apparently fighting it, resembled something from the deepest pits of Hell. They thundered into the living room and squashed the couch with their combined weight and velocity. Outside, Avalon could hear the screeching of at least one more of those black-armored things while another answered from the kitchen.

She watched as the creature she faced jumped back and loosed a roar of defiance at the newcomer. The one that seemed to have the upper hand was almost entirely black, with both skin and hair equally dark. It had some kind of chain-like things snaking from its wrists around the arms and shoulders of the pinned black-armored creature. Its hands were somewhat buried within the faceplate of the struggling monster beneath it. This thing looked like some demonic cross between a monstrous bat and a man.

Gabriel gave the living room a quick sweep and saw the other Hound as well as the Nightbane he expected to find. She was not, however, what he expected to see! Astoundingly beautiful, Gabriel's rage began to ebb at the sight of her! Angelic, dove-like wings sprouted from her back, the white feathers ending in black tips. Aside from this sole feature, she appeared human, which was very odd for a Nightbane. All of the ones Gabriel had ever met were ugly as hell. She must have been the exception to the rule.

The Hound had apparently killed an older woman, likely the Nightbane's parent, and now turned its attention towards the lovely Nightbane. Perhaps Gabriel arrived in a nick of time or perhaps the angelic woman had managed to hold it at bay for a few moments, but either way she appeared unharmed for now, at least. The struggling Hound beneath him stopped his appraisal by bucking wildly and forcing Gabriel to either fight it or let go.

Taking advantage of her foe's distraction, Avalon moved with impressive speed as she cambered her right leg while pivoting. Cutting loose with all of her newfound strength, she unleashed a potent roundhouse kick to the Hound's head. Avalon felt the impact and wondered how she didn't break every bone in her foot! The attack was like a sledgehammer pounding the murdering creature's temple. She turned a complete circuit as the kick followed through and was back into her ready stance in the blink of an eye. The Hound howled as its head and upper body were blasted violently to the side! It stumbled about to keep from being knocked prone from the unexpected attack. Hands flailing wildly for balance, it managed to avoid falling, but the metallic helmet, if that's what it was, held a truly impressive indentation of Avalon's foot right at the temple area.

Gabriel saw the attack from the corner of his eyes and had to give the girl credit. He was one of the more graceful and powerful beings compared to those he met over the years, with agility far beyond any Olympic athlete. Yet when he saw the ease of her attack and the power behind the blow, Gabriel was duly impressed. He wanted to watch more, but his pinned Hound had other ideas as it began to thrash about once more. The Hound bucked Gabriel to try and tear him off his perch so the Necrosis rolled with it. With grace that rivaled the lovely Nightbane, he released his claws and tendrils all in one quick move and rode the shove. Rolling in a tight ball, he flipped and landed lightly on the balls of his feet next to the Hound as it struggled to rise. With mere thought, Gabriel summoned forth one of his more formidable powers, creating a black, crackling blade of pure psychic energy in his right hand. The massive holes in the Hound's chest, head and shoulders produced a fair amount of some foul liquid - perhaps blood - that began to roll down its legs and onto the carpet. The Hound lashed out at Gabriel wildly and the Necrosis met the solid punch with his Psi-Sword. Forcing the Hound's arm out wide in his parry, the move opened the entire chest for his retaliation and Gabriel never slowed his momentum. He drove the humming blade deep into the Hound's armor and felt the thing shudder from the impact.

Metal cracked and the thing made a pathetic attempt at a screech, but it seemed to be losing much of its strength already. Jerking the energy blade free, Gabriel drew back again and decapitated the mortally wounded Hound with ease.

Avalon's foe recovered from the brutal hit and drew back for a swing with its axe. She instinctively knew that it would be a tough attack to dodge or parry, but she had to try. Stepping forward to try and catch the haft of the weapon, the Hound must have anticipated the move and stepped back as it swung. Avalon felt the fiery warmth of her own blood as the razor-sharp blade opened a painful gash along her upper thigh from the shortened attack. She groaned from the strike and felt the obvious strength of the creature, but it amazed her that the wound did not hurt more. Yes, it hurt, but it certainly was not debilitating by any means. In fact, she injured herself worse falling from the parallel bars last year in her gymnastics class! As insane as it sounded, she could swear she felt her wound already re-knitting itself! She and her foe stood a little more wary in front of each other, both sporting obvious injuries now.

Outside the house, the remaining Hound reached the front door and began to howl in bloodlust at the sight of an Athanatos and Nightbane both within killing range. The last of the group was in the kitchen and Gabriel could see it now from his vantage point. He knew they were outmatched. With the fight now slipping into three-on-two odds, and only one of the three injured, they would be in trouble. The girl was skilled and she was obviously not afraid to take the fight to the Hounds, but she didn't know the Hounds like he did. The Darkblades they carried were made of an otherworldly metal from the Nightlands. In addition to being crafted by magical means, the Darkblades were able to cut through the steel of a tank like butter! One solid hit from those axes would be lethal to either of them. She might get lucky or have enough skill to defeat her Hound, and Gabriel could definitely take out the one coming out of the kitchen, but the last Hound coming through the ruined front door posed a huge problem. Having just arrived back on Earth after his lengthy exile, Gabriel didn't have the energy to take on two healthy Hounds at once.

"The window!" he shouted at Avalon, hoping the girl would understand his intentions. Grabbing the dead Hound at his feet, Gabriel hurled it with all his might. The corpse slammed into the windows and wall with magnificent force, making an impressive hole. No only did it surprise the Hounds, it served to give them an escape route. Cancelling his Psi-Sword with a thought, Gabriel rushed at the woman, dodging a swing of her Hound's deadly axe as he enveloped her in a tackle that sent them both tumbling through the newly created exit. Despite her newfound agility, she was too shocked by the action to dodge him.

Past the bushes and onto the front lawn they rolled, both tucking instinctively into tight balls and rolling fluidly onto their feet. Gabriel dropped into a crouch between her and house and he shouted again. "Fly! I'll be right behind you!"

She stared at him in confusion for a moment before suddenly noticing her wings for the first time. Gabriel growled fiercely as the Hounds began to regroup and pour out of the exits of the house. Avalon remained still, flapping her dove-like wings gently as she seemed to be both entranced and horrified by what she was doing.

"GO!" Gabriel bellowed again, snapping her from the stupor.

She saw the creatures rushing towards them and instinctively dropped into a crouch. With a quick hop and a snap of her power-

ful wings, Avalon was airborne. The euphoric sensation of the cold air rushing past her was crushed by the overwhelming despair that was now crowding her thoughts. Adrenaline kept her mind focused on the fight instead of the horrors she witnessed, but now that she was calmed it all came pouring back in perfect clarity.

Her mother was dead.

Nothing else seemed to matter in that terrible moment. She flew with these strange, fantastic wings as a reflex as her mind focused solely on the memory of Carolyn's tragic death and the subsequent fight. What the hell was she to be able to turn into this... thing? Certainly not human, but then what? And what were those armored things with the strange weapons and inhuman screams? Her skin crawled and a shudder ran down her spine as she heard the warbling howls of those vicious monsters from behind her. They prowled around the lawn, three of them, gesturing fiercely at her and her strange-hued savior as they rocketed away. So focused on them, Avalon had barely noticed the dark speck in the shadowy night bearing down on her. Whatever he was, he had helped her. He looked like something from a Hellraiser movie, but she knew without a doubt that she would be dead too if he had not come along. The dark being flew amazingly fast, catching up with her in less than a quarter of a mile. Chains, if that's what they were, dangled from his wrists, but that odd crackling sword was gone now. She could barely see the whites of his teeth and eyes amid that onyx skin, but he did not seem to be approaching her in a hostile fashion.

Gabriel could hear the taunting cries of the remaining Hounds and he wanted to take one of the monsters up and drop it. But he knew that such an attempt would slow him down in his escape and they could easily injure him enough with a lucky shot to keep him from flying. He would be in dire trouble outnumbered three to one. Ahead, the winged Nightbane flew at a quick pace, but slower than what Gabriel could do if he weren't exhausted. His top speed was approximately 70 miles per hour and she seemed to be flying about half of that. Perhaps this was all new to her. Gabriel really had no idea if she had ever changed before that day or not. He caught up and saw her glancing back at him warily. Gabriel knew his appearance in his Gregorian form was highly intimidating and would possibly terrify her, but there was little he could do about that now. They might have to fight again before they could rest, and he wanted to be in peak shape for any such combat. His injuries were minor now, but he would not start to heal until he could find a place to land and rest. Besides, he thought, she looked like she could use a sanity break, too.

* * *

"Nightbane?" Avalon asked after Gabriel's initial explanations.

He nodded once. Since landing, Gabriel had shifted into his human form even though it forced him to maintain a certain level of concentration. Unlike a Nightbane, whose "normal" form was their human one, Gabriel's people were the opposite. Their Gregorian form was their natural one and they had to focus to maintain a human appearance. It seemed to calm Avalon down enough to speak with him rationally. Gabriel even eased her into her own transformation back to her human form which the Nightbane referred to as their Facade.

"There's no doubt," Gabriel pressed. "I've met many of your people over the years. I have no doubt that's what you are."

It amazed Gabriel that she looked only slightly different in her Facade than she did in her Morphus form. She lost the wings, obviously, but that extraordinary beauty she possessed – no, radiated – was still there. She shrunk a few inches during the change but otherwise looked very much the same. Her emerald eyes were tinged with redness from crying over her mother's death, and her shoulder-length auburn hair was somewhat disheveled from the flying, but she was amazingly beautiful regardless. He had a difficult time not staring.

Avalon considered his explanation for a moment. Too much was happening and her mind simply refused to process it all. Carolyn's death, her physical changes, the fight, Gabriel... it was all too much, too soon. She put her face in her hands and tried to fight back the next wave of tears.

Gabriel looked at the blank, dark sky and frowned. It was too much like the Nightlands in his opinion. Avalon had told him a little of recent events, such as the fact this phenomenon happened just minutes before his own arrival back on Earth. He left the part about the Nightlands out of his own story, mainly because he didn't wish to broach the subjects of alternate realities and demonic denizens of that hellish world just yet. He doubted she would be able to handle it. Gabriel left the girl to her misery for the moment, unable to think of anything comforting to say. It wasn't that Gabriel was heartless, rather he had little practice these past five decades showing empathy to anyone or anything. For him to have bothered with her rescue was amazing given everything he had experienced during his incarceration. Perhaps some part of his tortured mind realized a Nightbane was doomed and the outrage he felt sought to help. No one came to his aid, but that didn't mean he could not come to the aid of others.

"We should go," Gabriel said at length, and Avalon looked up from her weeping.

"Where?" she asked in a near whisper. Her tone was one of defeat.

"There are others like us. We should find them. Strength in numbers, yes?"

Avalon nodded slowly, too numbed by her grief to even care.

"The light in the distance," Gabriel said, gesturing to the northwest, "is Pittsburgh, if my geography is right. We can find help there, I hope. At the least we can find a better place to rest than this rooftop. The enemy has flying creatures called Hunters. Last thing we need is for a flock to spot us out in the open like this."

That seemed to spur Avalon as she stared into the starless sky as if expecting to see these Hunters swooping down on them right then. "I should have my leg looked at by a doctor," she said, though her words drifted off towards the end. Avalon tried to find the place on her thigh where the Hound's axe blade cut her, but there was nary a mark. Her jeans were ripped and there was blood on the fabric, but her leg itself showed no hint of injury.

Gabriel gave a genuine smile for the first time in five decades. "Nightbane heal quickly," he said, as if that explained everything. "It's faster in your Morphus, but your human Facade will heal quicker now, too."

Within moments the two shifted into their respective forms, Gregorian and Morphus, and were soaring through the quiet skies towards the distant city of Pittsburgh. Perhaps there the insanity that encompassed Johnstown would not be as bad, Avalon thought. She had no clue they were flying from the proverbial frying pan and into the fire. Only Gabriel, who was privy to some of the Ba'al's plans in the Nightlands, knew what to expect. Already the Athanatos was planning their next move. They needed information, and he suspected he might know a place to get it.

A.R.C.H.I.E. Phase 2
Optional Source Material for Rifts®
By Damon Sutton

"I think it's time, Hagan."
"Time for what, Arch?"
"It's time to start taking control."

Deep in the Aberdeen Proving Grounds, the artificial intelligence A.R.C.H.I.E. Three and his human 'idea man,' Hagan Lonovich, have been busy. The success of the Shemarrian Nation has moved the two from voyeurism to active participation in North American events. So far, the Shemarrian misdirection has been a rousing success. Archie and Hagan use the Shemarrians as warriors against Atlantis, scouts of the surrounding area, and glorious red herrings deflecting suspicion from their other activities. Local powers investigate the androids to dead end after dead end while Archie's other projects remain largely unhampered. Sales and distribution of Titan Robotics expand cautiously, encounters with local powers enhance Archie's technological prowess, and previously troublesome personalities (such as James T) are no more.

The Shemarrian Nation gives Archie space and time, but space and time are simply means to an end. That end is power. Archie and Hagan have managed to stake out a large amount of mostly uninhabited land, but the duo have decided to start experimenting with expanding. First to take control of some humans, and then to take control of humanity. World domination has ever been their goal, and the process towards that goal has moved into a more dynamic phase.

Misdirect, Evaluate, Infiltrate, Control

Archie and Hagan have a four part strategy. First, continue to keep the powers that be from having any idea about Archie's existence or strength. Misdirection has always been the most effective part of Archie's plans and it will continue to be so.

The second part is evaluation. Magic has always been a blind spot for Hagan and Archie. This is about to change. Archie realizes the common weaknesses of supernatural creatures to mundane items such as wood, fire, or silver. For centuries, humans have been fighting the supernatural using nothing but wits and knowledge. Archie is smarter than humans, therefore he should be even better at this. Archie may not be able to control magic, but he can control humans, which is the same thing to the enterprising dictator. As a result, Archie is gathering as much knowledge of the arcane as he can.

Archie will also be infiltrating the powers of North America. Technological powers such as the Coalition or Quebec will be child's play for Archie's electronic skill. Magical powers such as the Federation of Magic are more problematic, but Hagan has developed some ways around those difficulties. Hagan and Archie are particularly proud of their new line of 'spellcasting' androids. Atlantis with its alien mixture of both poses the greatest difficulty. In the short term, Archie's efforts to infiltrate Atlantis will be very slight, he is more focused on outright extermination.

Finally, Archie will begin to expand his control. Archie's goal is domination over the whole human race (for its own good of course). He will start exploring his ideas for the control of humans on a small scale. The isolated communities near the Shemarrian Nation will soon find themselves under the malevolent influence of a megalomaniacal computer. Some of them already have and don't even know it.

Strengthening the Illusion

The Shemarrian Nation has been an excellent red herring and the freedom that provides gives near endless flexibility. Archie and Hagan want to keep that ruse going and if possible, improve it. The Shemarrians are a good ploy, but Hagan is using his creativity to improve the inscrutability of the new "D-Bee" race. It is Hagan's hope that making small changes to the Shemarrians (such as the recent introduction of "males") will keep investigators off balance. The more confusing the Shemarrians are, the more likely efforts to understand them will come to naught. In addition, the more confusing they are, the more likely prying eyes will focus on them rather than on his other efforts.

Towards this goal, Hagan has been pondering more upgrades to the Shemarrians. The Shemarrians' greatest flaw is that they are androids and not alive in any way. Hagan has been taking steps in order to improve their semblance of life.

It started with the artifacts. The Shemarrians' frequent battles with the forces of Atlantis commonly yield magic items. At first, Archie didn't even have his androids bother taking spoils. However, curiosity eventually got the better of him and he started collecting. While the vast majority was useless and no amount of analysis was yielding any benefits, isolated cases of utility gave Archie promise. Furthermore, the employment of human "experts" yielded great knowledge, which led to great ambitions, and one particularly disastrous experiment with dimensional Rifts. Since then, Archie's efforts in the arcane area are now subtler. Archie and Hagan have decided to use smaller effects to bolster their plans.

Archie has learned that life fuels magic, which explains why his robotic efforts to use it have been fruitless. Yet although robots are not alive, they can *control* life. Archie's first step is the development of **Bio-Gel**. Bio-Gel is a microbial culture developed in Cyberworks' laboratories that he's using to bring a little vitality to his robotic minions. Archie has been incorporating it into his infiltration models in order to give them a semblance of life.

Bio-Gel is a green, viscous substance that smells slightly of leaves (the scent was Hagan's idea and leads to rumors that Shemarrians are part botanical). Ten pounds of Bio-Gel holds 1 P.P.E., and most Archie infiltration models (Shemarrians included) are installed with between ten and forty pounds of gel (1D4x10 pounds, which will give them 1D4 P.P.E.). This also gives the androids a crude, indistinct "aura" and "psychic scent" that can be detected by Psi-Stalkers, although both are incredibly weak and undeniably inhuman. This P.P.E. can be stolen freely by mages and *does not* double upon the "death" of the android.

New Androids

Hagan has been developing the Shemarrian society in order to give them depth and aid the illusion. The Shemarrian Hunters already suggest that they live in harmony with nature, and Hagan has decided to develop this in a cyber-druidic direction. As a result, Shemarrians not only ride bionic animals, but Shemarrian villages have tepees and trees with cybernetic implants. Metal cables intertwine with leaves and vines. Hagan has designed them to look like the Shemarrian cybernetic capacity expands to plants as well as animals. This illusion is compounded by the additions of the Seeress, Wyrding Tree, and Preserver.

Archie and Hagan are considering having the Shemarrians make contact with their enemies (such as the Republicans). This way, the enemies would believe they have a new ally in their fight against the robotic menace. Archie would then have the ally perform a betrayal at the worst instant, eliminating the threat. This plan is not in motion yet, but they could activate it at any time.

Shemarrian Seeress

The Shemarrians may be fierce warriors, but Hagan knows that eventually there will be interest in learning non-combat aspects of Shemarrian culture. If continued inquiries come up dry, great suspicion will arise as to the Shemarrians' methods. If Earth is to be their "home," then they will need something akin to villages and elders. His new plans keep giving investigators red herrings in order to deflect their true nature.

The Seeress fulfills this purpose. Seeresses act as shamans, healers and diplomats to any who visit the Nation. A frequent experience of captured visitors is an escort to a village, whereupon the Seeress will meet with them. She will talk with them, giving cryptic answers and kind words. She may even give them medical aid using the help of the Wyrding Tree. The other warriors will watch her and the visitors like hawks. If the visitors are respectful, they may be greeted, talked to, and escorted out. If otherwise, they will be killed.

The Seeress is subservient to any of the warrior classes and will explain gently to visitors that she is not in charge, she is only present on behalf of "the warring spirits." Any further questions will be calmly deflected with the phrase, "You have not yet earned our trust, but I truly sense you could one day."

Their knowledge of plants, animals, and cybernetics is encyclopedic, although they will express this knowledge in unusual terms. They discuss living things and machines as if they are one and the same, further cementing the druidic illusion.

Shemarrian Seeress

Model Type: A-SHE-25
Class: Fully Automated, Self Sufficient Diplomacy Robot.
Crew: None. Artificial Neural Intelligence.

M.D.C. by Location:
   *Antennae (2) – 10 each
   Hands (2) – 19 each
   Arms (2) – 30 each
   Legs (2) – 40 each
   *Head – 30
   Protective Ceremonial Headdress – 20
   **Main Body – 80

* A single asterisk indicates a difficult target to strike, requiring the attacker to make a *Called Shot*, and even then the attacker is -3 to hit (hitting an antenna is at -4).

Destroying the head of the robot eliminates all optics and sensory systems. Frequently, the robot will fall over and "play dead" if the head is destroyed, while surrounding units give a realistic impression of shock and anger. This is a ruse and if the situation warrants it (for example, the killers try to take the body away), the robot will lash out blindly (no bonuses to strike, parry, or dodge) until it is destroyed. **Note:** Damage to the head comes off the headdress first.

** Depleting the M.D.C. of the main body destroys the android, activating its internal destruct program. The 'Bot can wear human sized armor, but tends not to.

Speed:

Running: 90 mph (144 km) maximum. Note that the act of running does NOT tire the robot and can be maintained indefinitely.
Leaping: The robot's legs are strong and adequate for leaping. Leaps are limited to 10 feet (3 m) high and lengthwise. A running leap at speeds in excess of 40 mph (64 km) will enable the 'Bot to leap an additional 10 feet (3 m).
Flying: Possible only by use of a jet pack.
Range: The nuclear power pack gives the robot approximately 20 years of life, even under the most strenuous and constant amount of use.

Statistical Data:

Attribute Equivalents of Note: I.Q. 19, Robotic P.S. 30, P.P. 24, Synthetic P.B. 14+2D6 (varies), M.A. (Robotic diplomatic program) 16+1D4, Spd 132 (90 mph/144 km).
P.P.E.: 3 (Bio-Gel implantation).
Height: 7 feet (2.1 m).
Width: 3 feet (0.9 m).
Length: 2 feet, 5 inches (0.75 m).
Weight: 600 lbs (270 kg).
Physical Strength: Robotic P.S. of 30.
Cargo: The Seeress carries internal compartments in which herbs and small medical devices are stored (one on each arm and leg).
Power System: Nuclear, average 'Bot energy life is twenty years.
Black Market Cost: Not available.

Shemarrian Seeress Weapon Systems:

The Seeress has a series of innate weapon systems designed to look like spells. Archie and Hagan have figured that if a Shemarrian is perceived as casting spells, it is much less likely anyone would deduce their true nature. As a result, "spell-like" weapons systems were installed into the Seeress. These systems were designed to replicate spells as closely as possible and under the rigors of combat, most opponents wont know the difference. She will add magic incantations to her actions (with a 75% chance of having the correct incantation) in order to add authenticity, but these incantations are not needed.

1. **"Flash" Stun Device:** In the left palm of the Seeress is a bright light emitter that can flash in order to blind and disorient foes. The flash is a brilliant green and can blind foes up to 10 feet (3 m) away. Enemies who have light filters or some other type of light protection are immune. All others must make a save vs a 14 (Physical Endurance bonus applicable, other bonuses against magic are not). The Seeress accompanies this with motions and sounds similar to a Ley Line Walker casting Blinding Flash.

Primary Purpose: Disorientation.

Secondary Purpose: Defense.

Range: 10 feet (3 m).

Mega-Damage: None.

Rate of Fire: Each flash uses one melee attack.

Payload: Unlimited.

2. **Concealed Plasma Emitter:** In the right palm of the Seeress is a concealed short-range plasma emitter. Via intense scrutiny (and vivisection) of magic users, Archie has managed to develop a plasma blast of equal intensity and range to the Fire Bolt spell. The Seeress adds chanting and hand motions consistent with such a spell. If closely examined, magic users who know this spell can make a Perception Roll vs a 17 (I.Q. bonus applied) in order to determine that "something is missing" from the Fire Bolt, although the recipient of the blast may not agree with that assessment.

Primary Purpose: Anti-Personnel.

Secondary Purpose: Assault.

Range: 200 feet (61 m).

Mega-Damage: 4D6 M.D. per single blast.

Rate of Fire: 3 blasts per melee; each uses one of the robot's attacks.

Payload: Unlimited; fueled by the robot's internal power source.

3. **May Use Any Type of Common or Shemarrian Weapon:** These robots are humanoid and can use any weapons usable by humanoids.

4. **Hand to Hand Combat:** Skill is about equal to an eighth level Martial Artist.

Attacks per Melee: Seven.

Damage: As per Robot Strength of 30.

   Controlled S.D.C. Punch: 2D6+15 S.D.C.

   Restrained Punch: 1D4 M.D.

   Full Strength Punch: 2D6 M.D.

   Power Punch: 4D6 M.D. (but counts as two attacks).

Bonuses (all): +3 on initiative, +7 to strike, +9 to parry, +9 to dodge, +4 to roll with impact/fall, +2 to disarm, +5 to pull punch, +2 entangle, Critical Strike on a Natural 18-20, Paired Weapons, Leap Attack and Karate Kick. +6 to strike using Shemarrian rail guns, +4 to strike when using most other ranged weapons (as per W.P.). +1 on Perception Rolls.

5. **Sensors and Features of Note (in the head): Optics:** All the standard features of an Archie 'Bot plus the following: Passive light amplification (nightvision 2,000 feet/610 m) and thermal imaging (2,000 feet/610 m). Also has a full medical sensor suite giving the capabilities of a Portable Bio-Scan & Bio-Lab (see *Rifts® Ultimate Edition*, page 263).

   Antennae: All Shemarrian have two antennae, and ranking officers/leaders have a third. These ultra-sensitive sensor units function as motion and heat detectors as well as feelers (the antennae can move and touch things independent of each other, like a bug). Thus the penalty for being blind is only -3 to strike, parry, and dodge. The antennae will sense any incoming attacks from behind (normal dodge or parry applies), the Shemarrian will know how many people are behind and to the side within a 20 foot (6.1 m) radius and if any of them move toward her. The antennae can also sense air temperature within 1D4 degrees, the source of heat or cold, wind speed, humidity, altitude compared to sea level, and rate of speed via transport.

   Speech: Full vocal capabilities with a soft, human sounding, feminine voice. Speaks, reads, and understands the common languages as well as over 30 pre-Rifts languages. Also speaks (but can not read) Dragonese and Splugorth at 80%, and Faerie Speak at 60%.

   Self-Destruct Program: To help make the Shemarrian appear to be a living creature, she does not explode when all the main body M.D.C. is destroyed, but all internal systems burn and melt via a contained plasma blast that turns the insides into a dark green, oozing liquid reminiscent of melted plastic.

6. **Skill Programs:** All standard Shemarrian skill programs, plus Holistic Medicine, Medical Doctor, Cybernetic Medicine, Botany, Biology, Robot Mechanics, Weapons Engineer, Mechanical Engineer, and Chemistry, all at 85%. The Seeress uses these skills to aid travelers, and performs them alongside chants spoken in a poetic mixture of Dragonese and Faerie Speak.

Shemarrian Wyrding Trees

Shemarrian villages are dotted with cybernetic trees. The cybernetic implants are consistent with the bionic nature of the Shemarrians. They also allow Archie to place listening devices all over the village without the need for the more humanoid android units. To the outside observer, the trees appear to be a perfect blend of cybernetics and botanicals. Prehensile wire tendrils and vines writhe rhythmically, seeming to respond to the movements of the surrounding Shemarrians.

The Wyrding Tree looks like a bionic willow tree. Prehensile cybernetic tendrils mix with biological vines. The tree flashes and clicks, seeming to communicate with its Shemarrian cohorts via some sort of strange plant-like language. It acts as a "hospital" or "repair bay" for Shemarrians and their mounts. It can also tend other living creatures, cyborgs, and armor/weapons.

The trained eye, however, will observe the pairing of cybernetics and plants to be one-sided. An Cybernetic Medicine skill check (+20% if the character also has the Botany skill) will reveal that the botanical components of the trees serve no real function and that the cyborg components would be completely functional even if the botanical portion were not present. Characters with a druidic background will feel uncomfortable, and communion with the Wyrding Trees will reveal that they are in pain. Nanofibers impregnate the very leaves, and to the rare few who can hear it, the plant is screaming in agony.

Shemarrian Wyrding Tree

Model Type: A-SHE-26

Class: Auxiliary Sensory Drone.

Crew: None. Artificial Drone Intelligence.

M.D.C. by Location:
  *Cyber-Vines (20) – 20 each
  *Sensory Tendrils (20) – 15 each
  **Main Body – 400

  * A single asterisk indicates a difficult target to strike, requiring the attacker to make a *Called Shot*, and even then the attacker is -3 to hit.

  ** Depleting the M.D.C. of the main body destroys the unit, activating its internal destruct program.

Speed:
Running: Stationary, can not run.
Leaping: Stationary, can not leap.
Flying: Impossible.
Range: The nuclear power pack gives the robot approximately 20 years of life, even under the most strenuous and constant amount of use.

Statistical Data:
Attribute Equivalents of Note: Robotic P.S. 36, P.P. 24.
P.P.E.: 6 (Bio-Gel implantation).
Height: 21 feet (6.4 m).
Width: 9 feet (2.7 m).
Length: 9 feet (2.7 m).
Weight: 4,000 pounds (1,800 kg).
Physical Strength: Robotic P.S. of 36.
Cargo: None.
Power System: Nuclear, average 'Bot energy life is twenty years.
Black Market Cost: Not available.

Wyrding Tree Weapon Systems:
  Wyrding Trees are primarily sensory and medical/repair units. The following statistics are for the occasions it is asked to attack aggressively. However, in general, the purpose of the tree is to aid in repairs and medical care.
1. **Vibro-Scalpels (5):** The ends of the tendrils have scalpels around which a high-frequency field can be activated when needed.
   Primary Purpose: Surgical Assistance.
Secondary Purpose: Defense.
Range: 50 foot (15.2 m) reach.
Mega-Damage: 1D4+25 S.D.C. when the Vibro field is not activated, 1D6 M.D. when Vibro field is activated.
Payload: Unlimited.
2. **Laser Welding Torches (15):** Many tendrils have a laser torch on the end used for welding.
Primary Purpose: Cybernetics Repair.
Secondary Purpose: Defense.
Range: 50 foot (15.2 m) reach.
Mega-Damage: 1 M.D. per hit.
Payload: Unlimited.
3. **Hand to Hand Combat:** Skill is about equal to an eighth level Martial Artist.
Attacks per Melee: Seven.
Damage: As per Robot Strength of 30.
   Controlled S.D.C. Punch/Lash: 2D6+15 S.D.C.
   Full Strength Punch/Lash: 1D4 M.D.
Bonuses (all): +3 on initiative, +7 to strike, +9 to parry, no dodge, no roll with impact/fall, +2 to disarm, +5 to pull punch, +5 to entangle.

4. Sensors of Note: Optics: All the standard features of an Archie 'Bot plus the following: Passive light amplification (nightvision 2,000 feet/610 m) and thermal imaging (2,000 feet/610 m). Also has a full medical sensor suite, giving the capabilities of a Portable Bio-Scan & Bio-Lab (see *Rifts® Ultimate Edition*, page 263). Has full 360 degree vision due to sensors being on every tendril.

Speech: Can not speak, communicates with other Shemarrians via encrypted radio transmissions.

Self-Destruct Program: To help make the Wyrding Tree appear to be a living creature, it does not explode when all the main body M.D.C. is destroyed, but all internal systems burn and melt via a contained plasma blast that turns the insides into a dark green, oozing liquid reminiscent of melted plastic.

5. Skill Programs: The Wyrding Tree is an access unit that can be programmed by a Seeress to "take care" of visitors. A Seeress using a Wyrding Tree can attend to ten patients at once, administering aid or repairs to all simultaneously with one skill check.

Shemarrian Preserver

Similar to the Wyrding Tree, the Preserver is a cybernetic botanical construct. The Preserver acts as a sentry and when activated, serves the role of a giant robot. When dormant, they appear as incredibly thick trees (much like redwoods). However, when activated, a barrel chested humanoid blend of metal, wood, and leaf emerges to lay waste to all around it with energy beams, rail guns, and pummeling fists. Preservers are, at the moment, the physically largest members of the Shemarrian community, but Hagan and Archie are always brainstorming for bigger and better.

The Preserver's botanical portions are merely for show and do not affect the regular functioning of the robot. When these portions are eliminated, the robot is programmed to "play dead" in order to push the illusion that it is a cyborg. This is only faking, and if circumstances require the robot to fight beyond this point, it certainly can and will.

Shemarrian Preserver

Model Type: A-ES-2
Class: Fully Automated, Self Sufficient Infantry Robot.
Crew: None. Artificial Neural Intelligence.
M.D.C. by Location:

   *Antennae (2) – 20 each
   Hands (2) – 100 each
   Arms (2) – 300 each
   Legs (2) – 800 each
   Forearm Mounted Rail Guns (4) – 300
   *Head (reinforced) – 400
   **Main Body – 800

* A single asterisk indicates a difficult target to strike, requiring the attacker to make a *Called Shot*, and even then the attacker is -3 to hit (hitting an antenna is at -4).

Destroying the head of the robot eliminates all optics and sensory systems. When this happens, the robot will lash out blindly (no bonuses to strike, parry, or dodge) until it is destroyed.

** Depleting the M.D.C. of the main body destroys the robot, activating its internal destruct program.

Speed:

<u>Running</u>: 90 mph (144 km) maximum. Note that the act of running does NOT tire the robot and can be maintained indefinitely.

<u>Leaping</u>: The robot's legs are strong and adequate for leaping. Leaps are limited to 30 feet (9 m) high and lengthwise. A running start at speeds in excess of 40 mph (64 km) will enable the 'Bot to leap an additional 30 feet (9 m).

<u>Flying</u>: Possible only by use of a jet pack.

<u>Range</u>: The nuclear power pack gives the robot approximately twenty years of life, even under the most strenuous and constant amount of use.

Statistical Data:

<u>Attribute Equivalents of Note</u>: I.Q. 15, Robotic P.S. 60, P.P. 24, Synthetic P.B. 10, M.A., Spd 132 (90 mph/144 km).

<u>P.P.E.</u>: 40 (Bio-Gel implantation).

<u>Height</u>: 30 feet (9.1 m).

<u>Width</u>: 14 feet (4.3 m).

<u>Length</u>: 14 feet (4.3 m).

<u>Weight</u>: 40 tons.

<u>Physical Strength</u>: Robotic P.S. of 60.

<u>Cargo</u>: None internal, although the Preserver can carry passengers on its back.

<u>Power System</u>: Nuclear, average 'Bot energy life is twenty years.

<u>Black Market Cost</u>: Not available.

Shemarrian Preserver Weapon Systems:

The Preserver is a blunt instrument. Pummeling fists augmented with rail guns and energy blasts. Archie has designed its movements to mimic those of a Federation of Magic automaton as another red herring to obscure its true nature.

1. Shemarrian 6000 Rail Guns (4): On each forearm are two Shemarrian rail guns. Used in concert, these guns make the Preserver the equal of any similarly sized robot fielded in North America.

<u>Primary Purpose</u>: Anti-Armor and Anti-Vehicle.

<u>Secondary Purpose</u>: Assault.

<u>Range</u>: 6,000 feet (1,828 m).

<u>Mega-Damage</u>: 2D6x10 per single blast or 4D6x10 M.D. per double blast. (Each arm can fire its two guns simultaneously at a single target. Triple or quadruple blasts are not possible.)

<u>Rate of Fire</u>: Each single or double blast uses one of the robot's attacks.

<u>Payload</u>: 220 rounds per rail gun (880 total), stored in hidden compartments within the arms.

2. Plasma Emitters (2): Hidden in the chest are plasma emitters, designed to fire the plasma such that it appears to come from the wooden portions of the chest. Unskilled observers will think this is some sort of magic ability of the Preserver, but the more observant will be able to detect the hidden robotic source with a successful Robot Mechanics check.

<u>Primary Purpose</u>: Anti-Personnel.

<u>Secondary Purpose</u>: Anti-Vehicle.

<u>Range</u>: 2,000 feet (610 m).

<u>Mega-Damage</u>: 4D6 for single blast or 8D6 M.D. per double blast.

<u>Rate of Fire</u>: Each single or double blast uses one attack.

<u>Payload</u>: Unlimited; fueled by the robot's internal power source.

3. Hand to Hand Combat: Skill is about equal to an eighth level Martial Artist.

<u>Attacks per Melee</u>: 6

<u>Damage</u>: As per Robot Strength of 60.

   Controlled S.D.C. Punch: 4D6+45 S.D.C.

   Restrained Punch: 2D4 M.D.

   Full Strength Punch: 4D6 M.D.

   Power Punch: 8D6 M.D. (but counts as two attacks).

<u>Bonuses (all)</u>: +3 on initiative, +7 to strike, +9 to parry, +4 to dodge, +4 to roll with impact/fall, +2 to disarm, +5 to pull punch, +2 to entangle, Critical Strike on a Natural 18-20, Paired Weapons, Leap Attack and Karate Kick. +6 to strike using Shemarrian Rail Guns, +4 to strike when using most other ranged weapons (as per W.P.). +1 on Perception Rolls.

4. Sensors of Note (in the head): Optics: All the standard features of an Archie 'Bot plus the following: Passive light amplification (nightvision 2,000 feet/610 m) and thermal imaging (2,000 feet/610 m).

   Antennae: The Preserver's antennae look like waving, cybernetic vines. These ultra-sensitive sensor units function as motion and heat detectors as well as feelers (the antennae can move and touch things independent of each other, like a bug). Thus the penalty for being blind is only -3 to strike, parry, and dodge. The antennae will sense any incoming attacks from behind (normal dodge or parry applies), and the robot will know how many people are behind and to the side within a 20 foot (6.1 m) radius and if any of them move toward it. The antennae can also sense air temperature within 1D4 degrees, the source of heat or cold, wind speed, humidity, altitude compared to sea level, and rate of speed via transport.

   Speech: Full vocal capabilities with a deep, masculine sounding voice. Phrases are kept simple.

   Self-Destruct Program: To help make the Preserver appear to be a living creature, it does not explode when all the main body M.D.C. is destroyed, but all internal systems burn and melt via a contained plasma blast that turns the insides into a dark green, oozing liquid reminiscent of melted plastic.

5. Skill Programs: All standard Shemarrian skill programs.

Learning About the Supernatural

Archie and Hagan were chastened by recent experiments in magic and have decided to make more subtle forays into the mystic arts. Archie has come to the conclusion that despite recent failures, he will need to address magic if he is ever going to rule humanity. Magic is on Earth to stay, and only by accepting that can Archie's ambitions come to fruition. Unfortunately, robots can't use magic (although skillfully designed androids can certainly give the appearance). Archie instead focuses on the ability for robots to do what they can do. Understand, manipulate, and control.

Obtaining Test Subjects

Archie's first effort was to understand magic. Shemarrians and other units recruit "candidates" for Archie's experiments. Archie handles this carefully (due to magic's unpredictable nature). No more does Archie crudely hire mages through 3rd parties, he instead acts with more initiative.

Archie initially used agents to hire mercenary mages in order to study them. These experiments on willing subjects proved unproductive since subjects tended to deceive (in order to receive more payment) or mislead (in order to gain some sort of leg up upon their mysterious employer), making their information unreliable.

As a result, Archie now uses a more aggressive recruitment strategy. His forces leave most mages alone, but if a target appears to be vulnerable (by traveling alone or in a small/poorly armed group), Archie sends a robot squad to "retrieve" the mage. The squad attacks suddenly, without mercy, with their goal being the subduing of the mage and the extermination of anyone around him. The process is designed to have as few witnesses as possible. Hagan suggested the outfitting of the retrieval drones in Coalition armor, and Archie loved it! The rare survivors of these attacks report sudden strikes of Coalition soldiers on groups containing mages, and no one thinks anything strange beyond the possible presence of unusually enthusiastic CS mage-hunters. Archie has been using groups of A-49 combat drones for this purpose (use published statistics, but add 50-80 M.D.C. for their Coalition armor).

Once captured, the robots take the mages to one of Archie's underground facilities. There he implants the mages with cybernetics designed to keep them under control (see below).

AHES-14 Monitoring System

Archie has designed a series of devices for the purpose of the monitoring and control of humans. Based loosely on the IRMSS, Archie's Human Enforcement System (AHES) is a system of implants placed in an electronic web throughout the subject. Small implants (ranging in size from 0.5 to 2 cm in diameter) are placed in the brain, bone marrow, glands, and major nerve clusters of the body. These implants communicate with one another using radio transmissions and micro-robots circulating in the bloodstream. Archie has designed the implants for non-augmented humans, and never attempts to implant them in non-humans or augmented humans.

Archie uses the implants to radio orders to the subject. Interception of this transmission requires a successful Radio: Scramblers check (at -40% due to Archie's skill in hiding his transmissions). Archie tends to communicate with the subject using a voice that is designed to be soothing. Archie is still experimenting with the best voice for controlling humans. As a result, he still uses a diversity of voices (G.M.s should be free to pull out any voice for this purpose). People with enhanced hearing may hear a "murmur" coming from the head of the implant victim, and focused hearing may be able to catch individual commands (Perception Roll versus a 19).

The implants relay information to Archie and any of Archie's robots (including Shemarrians). They allow the monitoring of the subject's location and activity. They record every word, gesture, and action of the subject. They see/hear/feel everything the subject does. Smell and taste are not (yet) recorded. The implants in the limbic system also allow a monitoring of the emotional state of the subject. (Archie has a 98% chance of detecting strong emotions such as terror, rage, or lust. Less intense emotions like disdain or annoyance have only a 75% chance of detection.) Archie can also detect when the subject is lying (70% chance).

The implants can also "remind" the subject of his status. The AHES can be used to stimulate sensations in the subject, though currently, only two sensations have been implemented. The first is a reminding "prickly itch" induced by microelectrode stimulation to the nervous system. The second is agony caused by direct stimulation of the pain centers of the brain (victim must make a save vs pain with a target of 23 to avoid writhing in agony, add both P.E. and M.E. bonuses). Archie will frequently monitor the emotional state of the agonized victim to ensure that the reminder is having its desired effect. Unusually fearless subjects can only lead to trouble, so Archie often liquidates them early. Archie doesn't appreciate bravery in his slaves.

Finally, the implant can be used to kill the subject. The robots can be commanded directly to destroy the brain and central nervous system of the victim. Complete paralysis occurs within 3 seconds, and death occurs within 6 seconds. Once the subject is dead, the implants overheat and liquefy, causing rivulets of molten metal to flow out of smoking holes in the corpse at every implantation site.

Current victims of the implant must stay within monitoring range of A.R.C.H.I.E.-3 (within 200 miles/320 km of the Aberdeen facility) or within 200 feet (61 m) of an accompanying Archie 'Bot. Archie errs on the side of caution, so if the signal between the implants and Archie is broken for ANY reason (EMP, distance, freak electrical failure, etc.), the implants immediately activate the kill command. Archie is developing a series of rules that he uses on recipients of the implant. He informs recipients of the rules, but they are ever changing, and Archie worries a lot more about keeping his secrets safe than he does about any individual subject.

These are Archie's initial implant policies:

Lying: The first detected lie activates the prickly sensation and a stern "Are you telling me the whole truth?" from Archie. The second detected lie activates an immediate agony response. The third kills the victim. Archie frequently "loses count" of how many lies have been told by his subjects. When he does so, he immediately kills the victim. Admittedly, losing count is a rare problem for a computer to have, but Archie is not as dependable a computer as he would like.

Unauthorized Spell Use: If the subject tries to cast a spell, uses a psionic ability, or activates a supernatural effect (such as an artifact) without Archie's permission, Archie will activate the agony switch. If the subject ceases the effort, he will be warned not to attempt that again. If the subject continues to cast the spell, Archie will simply activate the kill switch.

Discussion of Escape: The devices record every sight and sound of the victim. Any discussion of escape is punished with agony on the first offense and death on the second.

Detection of Implant: If any non-desired people make comments indicating suspicion of the implants (for example, if someone comments upon the victim's scars over every nerve cluster), the subject is given the prickly sensation and gently reminded to deflect suspicion. If the subject does not do so quickly and smoothly (or if the person making the comments keeps pressing the issue), Archie will commonly activate the kill command.

Attempted Removal of Implant: Any attempt to remove the implants by the subject or anyone around him will immediately result in activation of the kill command. The implants will respond even to the suggestion of an attempt. By the time a Cyber-

Doc has finished saying, "I am now going to remove the implant. Sit very still while I ..." the victim is already dead.

Manipulation of Implant: Archie and Hagan are both intimately familiar with abilities like Object Read and Telemechanics. As a result, any connection to the implants' programming, via hacking or Telemechanics, results in activation of the kill switch. The beginnings of any attempt activate the kill switch. If an attempt is made somehow without the subject's knowledge, hacking and Telemechanics checks are made at -40%. Keep in mind, before any attempts could be made to "hack" the implant, one would have to determine its presence without breaking the Detection rule.

Telepathic Contact: Telepathic contact has an 85% chance of detection for every 15 seconds it exists. Archie has yet to figure out how to determine the nature of the contact, but the implants can determine if it is occurring. Detection of Telepathic contact immediately activates the kill switch.

Deactivation of Implant: Sudden deactivation prevents the microbots from destroying the nervous system, but the caustic fluids are still released from the implants. Instead of the normal effects, the person feels the implants liquefy and burn themselves out of the brain, bones, and nerve clusters over the next twelve seconds. This does 1D4x100 Hit Points to the victim and usually leaves him crippled at best. If he survives, he is free of the implants. If Archie finds a victim who is likely to survive this, he doesn't implant him.

Designer's Note: The AHES system is a brutal one to say the least. I've designed it to be an unforgiving enforcement mechanism. Interactions with NPCs carrying this system will be tense, as the victims often know the enormity of the implants. Game Masters may be tempted to install this system unwillingly into player characters, but they must temper this temptation with wisdom. No player likes to have his character's brains melt out of his body in a puddle of caustic ooze.

Spell Experimentation

Archie currently has 50 implanted human mages kept prisoner in Aberdeen. Hagan and Archie refer to this facility as "the Aberdeen Library" or just "the Library." If the subjects follow orders and behave, one could say that they have a relatively smooth existence, at least smooth by the standards of Rifts Earth. Frequently, he sends individuals out with escorts for information gathering missions. These subjects even have limited allowance to meet with local communities, however any bad behavior such as the discussion or hinting at their true status, is immediately punished. One mage attempted to blink SOS in Morse Code to a trader, and at the fifth blink, he was immediately killed. An A-63 attack squad subsequently exterminated the trading caravan, as well as the community they had just left and the community they were heading to. Archie informed the others in the Library of the extermination, and even made them watch a recording of some of the slaughter.

Archie commonly has his test subjects cast spells in front of intricate sensor arrays so that he may record the gestures and effects. They are also encouraged to discuss the arcane with one another (so long as escape is not discussed) so that Archie can record and evaluate. In some ways, the Aberdeen Library is a very active magical community, as Archie gives his subjects limited access to books and materials. Through this, Archie has developed an impressive amount of data on most of the spells available in North America.

Of course, Archie's knowledge is still rudimentary and he is always on the lookout for new and unusual spell casters for examination. Fatalities are also common in the Library, so robots are always looking for replacements.

Archie is very proud of this community, and sees it as a "test-run" for his future plans for humanity. All of Archie's robots are on the lookout for new recruits for the Aberdeen Library. Player characters could easily find themselves looking for a kidnaped compatriot (or worse yet, being hunted themselves for unusual magic capacity).

Spell Approximation

Archie is learning about the spells commonly used in North America. He and Hagan are also working on cybernetic equivalents of these spells for incorporation into infiltrator androids. His studies focus on Ley Line Walkers and Shifters, so his robots use the chants and gestures of these magic users. The vast majority of the witnesses of the spell casting can't tell the difference. Magic users who don't know the "spells" in question can roll a Perception Roll versus 19 to tell there's something unusual about the spells being cast. Knowing the spell brings the target number down to 17, with the spell caster getting the idea of something missing from the spell. If asked, the robots will mention something cryptic such as, "On our world, the energies are more subtle than here." Suspicion may remain, but when faced with a wizard, the last thing anyone on Rifts Earth suspects is a robot.

Archie has developed and installed approximations of the following spells into his robots. An A-51 Spybot can be equipped with 8 of these spell-like features. Hagan has dubbed these improved drones "Arch-Mages." These drones are programmed to be very secretive and mysterious in their spell casting.

Blinding Flash: Light emitters in the palm of the robot emit the flash. Victims must save versus a 17 (Physical Endurance bonus applies, other bonuses versus magic do not).

Cloud of Smoke: The robot closes its eyes and smoke emits from concealed vents throughout the robot. The robot holds 100 charges worth of smoke emitters. The size and effects of the smoke are identical to the spell.

See the Invisible: Infrared and ultraviolet optics are standard on all of Archie's robots, but mage drones are programmed to disregard this information unless they "cast" the spell. In this way, the drone seems to acquire the effect when in fact it had it all along.

Thunderclap: High-intensity speakers hidden in the head of the robot produce the sound. The spell casting, sound and effect of the thunderclap emitters are identical to those of the 4th level Shifter from whom Archie "learned" the spell.

Chameleon: The drone, robe, and staff are all covered in a color-changing synthetic skin that adapts to the surrounding environment. The effect takes 2 melee attacks to perform and gives the robot a 75% Prowl skill when the "spell" is active. This effect only works on the robot and can not be performed on other targets. If asked why, the robot will respond, "Meditate with me during the six-month Bruina ritual, and you would understand. Without this, any explanation I attempt would come to naught."

Climb: The robot meditates and then climbs with a 94% skill. Of course, the robot always had this level of climbing ability, but witnesses don't know this. This is also a spell that is commonly used by the Shemarrian Seeress upon other Shemarrians (in the rare case the target android can't climb, the Seeress uploads the climbing program into the subject android).

Concealment: The robot casts the spell and uses sleight of hand (84%) to place the object into hidden compartments on its person.

Heavy Breathing: Parabolic sonic emitters in the shoulders of the robot focus the sound at targets up to 100 feet (30.5 m) away. Effect is identical to the spell.

Armor of Ithan: This effect is very complex. Holographic and force field emitters around the android make the spell appear to happen. The resulting field only has 10 M.D.C. The spell was designed based upon observation of an 8th level Ley Line Walker. As a result, those knowledgeable in this spell may be surprised as to how weak the armor is in comparison to how it looks. The robot is also unable to have it affect anyone more than 10 feet (3 m) away.

Energy Bolt: The bolt comes from the fingers of the robot. It is resolved as a shooting attack. Damage is 4D6 S.D.C. The energy output and color of the blast are identical to a 2nd level Mystic.

Carpet of Adhesion: White mist fires from the hand of the robot. This white mist conceals the emission of a powerful adhesive that can be placed on the floor or wall of a structure. Range is 20 feet (6 m). Creatures with a P.S. of less than 15 are held fast if they touch the surface. Creatures with P.S. between 15 and 25 are slowed (-2 to dodge) if they are touching the surface. Those with P.S. above 25 or Supernatural Strength are not affected. This effect only works on solid surfaces; on loose sand, leaves or gravel it would only make a mess.

Energy Field: This effect works identically to the Armor of Ithan effect, it just has cosmetic differences to make it look like an Energy Field.

Magic Net: This effect is commonly installed into the staff of the A-51 Spybot. A concealed net springs from the staff. The net is a nano-fiber-enforced web covered in adhesive. The robot carries ten nets. It is immune to dispelling, but can be cut through with 40 M.D. worth of damage. A signal from the robot can cause the net to liquefy (similar to the self-destruct mechanism of a Shemarrian), destroying the net and doing 1D4 M.D. to anyone caught in it. The net looks for all practical purposes like a Magic Net (quantum fluorescent compounds are even impregnated into the fibers to make it glow), but mages will detect that it is not magical.

Fire Bolt: A plasma emitter in the palm fires the bolt. Damage and appearance are identical to the spell (4D6 M.D. or 1D6x10 S.D.C.).

Multiple Image: Holographic projectors produce the images, which are immune to being dispelled.

Circle of Flame: The robot appears to draw a line around itself with its staff, but it is actually depositing a specially formulated gel which then combusts into the circle. Damage is the same as the spell.

Energy Disruption: A small electromagnetic pulse (EMP) is generated to knock out the electronics of a system. Range is the same as the spell, but the effect is permanent.

Superhuman Strength, Superhuman Speed: These are effects that the robot fakes. A-51 drones will act as if they have a P.S. of 15 and a Spd of 23 until they "cast" these spells, at which point they will use their full strength and speed. They can not apply these effects to others, of course.

Apparition: Holographic projectors produce the image. The image can not be dispelled, however as a hologram, it is unable to do real damage. If someone plunges a rod of iron into the image, the robot will deactivate it, adding to the illusion of this being a spell.

Fire Ball: Specially modified miniature plasma grenades, with a flammable outer coating, are hidden in the robot. It throws them, doing 4D4 M.D. upon impact. The robot carries four such grenades.

Magic Pigeon: In a hidden compartment within the forearm of the robot is an android of a pigeon. This pigeon is actually a lifelike robotic drone (10 M.D.C., +3 to strike/parry/dodge). The robot carries two such drones, one in each arm.

Mask of Deceit: This effect is approximated by the installation of a system similar to the AA-1 Cyber Disguise (see page 236 of the original *Rifts® RPG*, or page 46 of the *Bionics Sourcebook*), with the exception that the robot only needs one melee round to disguise itself fully. The robot activates the system with chants and gestures similar to the spell.

Tongues: The robot acts as if it only speaks a few languages (American, Spanish), but after chants and gestures, it will demonstrate capacity in any of the 94 languages it is programmed with. This functions for all major human languages on Earth, plus Dragonese, Gobblely, and Faerie Speak. Other languages are not known yet, but Archie often seeks to capture speakers of new languages for this purpose.

Wind Rush: This "spell" is accompanied by a fog effect, which conceals the robot's revealing of jet-like protrusions that cause the Wind Rush. Range is only 20 feet.

Spoil: Capsules of virulent bacteria and pungent chemicals are installed into the fingertips of the robot. The robot inoculates the food or water by touching it and releasing the bacteria. Effects are identical to the spell, except that protection from magic does not prevent damage; instead the victim must save vs poison with a difficulty of 18.

Agony: The Agony spell is approximated by a small, high-intensity microwave device within the eyes of the robot. After 10 seconds, the victim feels a sense of heating all over his body. This sensation soon grows painful (a save vs poison with a difficulty of 19 is required or else he loses half his attacks and suffers a penalty of -1 to all combat actions due to the pain). If the microwaving continues, the target will take 2D6 S.D.C. every three seconds as the skin begins to bubble and cook. The A-51 drones use this as a method of torture on bound opponents. It has no effect on Mega-Damage opponents or people in fully environmental armor (but it does function if the head is not encased). Archie and Hagan are working to fix these deficiencies.

Familiar Link: A-51 Spybots with this "spell" are sent out with animal companions. These animal companions are actually lifelike robot animal facsimiles. Radio communication allows the drone to see through the eyes of the companion. If the companion is destroyed, the robot will seem to meditate while Archie sends a replacement. Archie is also experimenting with robots that are accompanied by living animals, although these animals are little more than exceedingly well-trained pets.

Summon and Control Rodents: While the robot draws the pentagram, hypersonic and pheromone emitters give a sound/scent that rodents find irresistible. Luckily, the prevalence of rats all over North America assures the effectiveness of the summoning. The rats then attack everyone in the vicinity. On occasion, Archie has created hundreds of android rats for one of his mages to summon and which would act under the control of the A-51 drone.

Summon Shadow Beast: This actually summons a specially made Archie construct. The Arch-beast has 40 M.D.C., does 2D6 M.D. per strike, and looks like a Shadow Beast (in the light). It will use a chameleon ability when in shadow, but this is the chameleon effect from above rather than a true Shadow Meld.

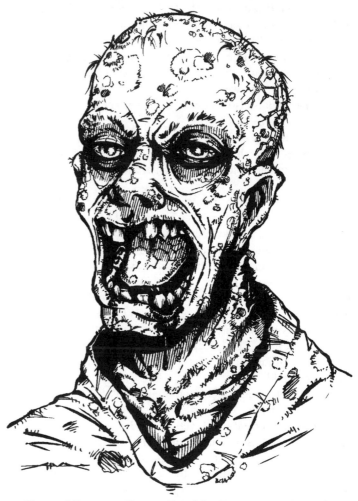

Create Mummy, Create Zombie: It turns out that animating corpses is not that difficult for Archie. The drone will obtain all the needed materials (bandages, ointments, etc.) for use on the corpse. In reality, it needs none of them. As it goes through the motions of the ritual, micro-scalpels within the hands of the drone implant a rudimentary endo-nanoskeleton into the corpse. The result is the impregnation of the corpse with a robotic web that animates it like a puppet on strings. It is essentially a light robot wearing a corpse. A rudimentary AI is installed, giving the "mummy" an I.Q. of 6. Archie is very proud that his mummies are smarter than the normal kind. The A-51 has enough implantable nano-fibers to create six such animated corpses. If a nearby mage notes the lack of P.P.E. or undead energy of the mummy, the drone will respond, "It is dead, what did you expect to sense?" The nano-fiber mesh is very delicate and if 100 S.D.C. worth of damage is done, the corpse falls. The A-51 drone will commonly give the animated corpses M.D.C. weapons and armor.

Robotically Animated Corpse (Mummy or Zombie): P.S. 15, P.P. 12, I.Q. 6. Four attacks per melee. +3 to strike, +4 to parry, +2 to dodge. +4 to strike with ranged weapons. 100 S.D.C. Basic optics and sensory systems (no advanced optics).

When near a greater robotic intelligence (for example, an A-51 Spybot), the animated corpse will cringe from holy symbols, protection wards, and holy utterances. If greater than 100 feet (30.5 m) from its guiding intelligence, the inborn AI is not sophisticated enough to remember such niceties, and will simply follow the last order given and then return to its master.

Other Spell-Like Effects: G.M.s are encouraged to think of other magical effects that can be approximated by the robots. Electric arcs, acid blasts, and electromagnetic "telekinesis" are all things that would work.

Infiltration

The upgraded A-51 Arch-Mage units are used to gather information in magic-heavy regions of North America. Several units have already joined rural communities as sages, where they provide spiritual guidance to the inhabitants. These units report all information to Archie via radio transmission or the Magic Pigeon effect.

As an experiment, one series of drones has built a community based on Archie's unique style of animated corpses. These drones, known as the "Coven of Ipswich," have enslaved the community and control it through fear and intimidation. It is Archie's hope that this area will serve to draw Necromancers, who Archie can then capture for the purposes of recruitment to the Aberdeen Library. Unfortunately, teams of do-gooders often stymie such efforts.

Archie is sending other A-51 drones into the outskirts of the Federation of Magic. These units are collegial to magical communities and willingly take roles that are low on the magical totem pole. In these roles, the drones can gather information while evading suspicion as they look like just another group of D-Bee mages seeking refuge from a genocidal Coalition. Archie is also infiltrating these areas with android rats and other android facsimiles of magical creatures so the A-51s can practice their summoning spells when needed. At the moment, the powers within the Federation are so focused on the Coalition (with its comparatively primitive robotic capabilities) that they have no suspicion of infiltration by advanced artificial intelligences. Their most ambitious plan to infiltrate so far involves the placement of a facsimile of an Automaton into a Federation storage facility. Archie has already created a robotic duplicate of an Earth Thunder Automaton and now seeks to smuggle it into Federation storage, where it can sit quietly in the storage house and send back information about the deployment of other Automatons.

The Hidden Holocaust

Archie wants to rule humanity, but he has no use for non humans. As a group, non-humans serve only as barriers to his ambitions. He has only one solution for intelligent non-humans whose very existence gets in the way of his plans: extermination. Once exterminated, however, could they then be useful? The liberation of a small community in Ohio proved the answer to that question to be "yes."

Massillon, Ohio was a community held under the brutal rule of a Thornhead Demon. The demon demanded offerings and worship from the human inhabitants in exchange for protection from outside threats. One night, a large squad of A-63 combat drones ambushed the demon in its cave. The robots used the advantage of surprise to kill the demon quickly and quietly. After killing the demon, they hid in the cave, awaiting the next night, when they would return to Aberdeen. Much to Archie's surprise, the community didn't notice their "benefactor" was dead, and instead continued to leave offerings at the mouth of the cave!

This inspired a plan. Soon after, the community again saw its Thornhead overlord. The demon's requests for food changed into demands for precious metals, and it no longer drank the blood of young girls, but it still killed any detractors and demanded permanent allegiance. The life of the community was unchanged, they had no idea that Archie had merely replaced their demon with an android duplicate. To this day, the community is brutally ruled via android proxy.

The elimination and replacement of a community of Brodkil was similarly effective at controlling nearby human settlements. The partially cyborg nature of these demons makes them particularly easy to duplicate. As a result, Archie murders them in large numbers. He meticulously replaces each murdered Brodkil with a robotic duplicate programmed to emulate the behavior of the demon. Archie sees through their eyes, controls their movements, and through these decoy bands he extends tendrils of influence far beyond his underground lair.

Archie and Hagan have designed a series of robots to emulate common supernatural threats. Although early tests with Brodkil were successful, Archie has developed a preference for android duplicates of more subtle menaces. Emulating these menaces allows Archie's use of misdirection, and provides an unwelcome surprise for liberators who arrive prepared for one threat and find themselves in trouble when it turns out to be something completely different. The new Arch-Vampire design performs that role perfectly.

Arch-Vampire

These androids stalk the distant wildernesses surrounding Lake Ontario. There, they gather information, terrorize local human communities, and if possible, kill non-human inhabitants of the area. They look like wild vampires, act like Wild Vampires, and to the untrained are indistinguishable from the real thing.

In fact, a small vampire outbreak had occurred in the area. Archie's scouts came across it and he decided to test his robotic intelligence against the forces of the undead. At first, the vampire clan thought it was being attacked by a rival clan, and the element of surprise was sufficient for the robots to completely exterminate the vampires before they truly knew what had hit them. The first test was a rousing success; the new model confused the enemies and showed amazing ability to destroy the undead plague. The robots were immune to vampiric mind control, did not sleep, and wielded silver weapons with lethal strength.

Arch-Vampire

Model Type: A-SUP-004
Class: Fully Automated Self Sufficient Reconnaissance and Extermination Unit.
Crew: None. Artificial Intelligence.

M.D.C. by Location:
Hands (2) – 20 each
Arms (2) – 50 each
Retractable Blade – 20
Legs (2) – 100 each
*Head – 50
**Main Body – 250
***Outer Skin – 5

* A single asterisk indicates a difficult target to strike, requiring the attacker to make a *Called Shot*, and even then the attacker is -3 to hit.

Destroying the head of the robot eliminates all optics and sensory systems. If this happens, the robot will lash out blindly (no bonuses to strike, parry, or dodge) until it is destroyed.

** Depleting the M.D.C. of the main body destroys the android, activating its internal destruct program. The 'Bot can wear human sized armor, but doesn't (after all, real vampires don't).

*** Mega-Damage attacks can damage the outer skin layer and reveal the true robotic nature of the android.

Speed:
Running: 90 mph (144 km) maximum. Note that the act of running does NOT tire the robot and can be maintained indefinitely.

Leaping: The robot's legs are strong and well suited for leaping. Leaps are limited to 20 feet (6 m) high or lengthwise. A running leap at speeds in excess of 40 mph (64 km) will enable the 'Bot to leap an additional 10 ft (3 m).

Flying: Possible only by use of a jet pack.

Range: The nuclear power pack gives the robot approximately 20 years of life, even under the most strenuous and constant amount of use.

Statistical Data:
Attribute Equivalents of Note: I.Q. 14, Robotic P.S. 36, P.P. 24, Synthetic P.B. 14+2D6 (varies), Spd 132 (90 mph/144 km).

P.P.E.: 3 (Bio-Gel implantation).

Height: 5-6 feet (2.1 m).

Width: 3 feet (0.9 m).

Length: 2 feet (0.6 m).

Weight: 300 lbs (135 kg).

Physical Strength: Robotic P.S. of 36.

Cargo: None.

Power System: Nuclear, average 'Bot energy life is twenty years.

Black Market Cost: Not available.

Arch-Vampire Weapon Systems and Features:
1. **Photodegradative Skin:** Arch-Vampires have a synthetic skin overlay that matches the shade and coloring of undead skin. Moreover, the skin has internal caustic micro-release systems that can be activated in order to produce an appearance of burning or smoking. These systems are commonly activated upon exposure of the robot to sunlight, water, wood, or silver. In addition, the unit will cringe and hiss upon being hit with these substances. The burning is only a cosmetic change and can be reversed over time (the robot uses the reversibility of this change to mimic the appearance of vampiric regeneration). In fact, sunlight, water, wood and silver do no damage to the robot at all, but it will make an excellent show and will often flee if too much exposure is received (if attacks would do more than 40 points of damage to a vampire, the Arch-Vamp will flee).

2. **Retractable Silver Blade:** In the right palm of the Arch-Vamp is a retractable silver blade. The robot's unnatural strength makes this blade a highly effective vampire killing weapon. The concealed nature of the weapon also aids in the surprise decapitation of vampiric foes.

Primary Purpose: Anti-Vampire.

Secondary Purpose: Anti-Supernatural.

Range: Melee; the blade is one foot (0.3 m) long.

Damage: 4D6+25 damage to vampires and other supernatural beings vulnerable to silver.

Rate of Fire: Equal to the number of attacks of the unit (8).

3. **Concealed Flamethrower:** In the left palm is a small flamethrower. The primary purpose of this is the cremation of decapitated vampires, but it is also effective against other creatures vulnerable to fire.

Primary Purpose: Anti-Vampire.

Secondary Purpose: Anti-Supernatural.

Range: 10 feet (3 m).

Damage: 3D6 S.D.C., plus a 60% chance to set combustibles ablaze. Vampires and other supernatural beings vulnerable to fire take damage as Hit Points, M.D.C., double damage, or whatever is appropriate.

Rate of Fire: Each blast uses one of the robot's attacks.

Payload: Unlimited; fueled by the robot's internal power source.

4. **May Use Any Type of Common or Shemarrian Weapon:** These robots are humanoid and can use any weapons usable by humanoids, but usually don't as it would be out of character.

5. **Hand to Hand Combat:** Skill is about equal to an eighth level Martial Artist.

Attacks per Melee: Eight.

Damage: As per Robot Strength of 30.

  Controlled S.D.C. Punch: 2D6+15 S.D.C.

  Restrained Punch: 1D4 M.D.

  Full Strength Punch: 2D6 M.D.

  Power Punch: 4D6 M.D. (but counts as two attacks).

Bonuses (all): +3 on initiative, +7 to strike, +9 to parry, +9 to dodge, +4 to roll with impact/fall, +2 to disarm, +5 to pull punch, +2 to entangle, Critical Strike on a Natural 18-20, Paired Weapons, Leap Attack and Karate Kick. +6 to strike using Shemarrian Rail Guns, +4 to strike when using most other ranged weapons (as per W.P.). +1 on Perception Rolls.

6. Sensors of Note (in the head): Optics: All the standard features of an Archie 'Bot plus the following: Passive light amplification (nightvision 2,000 feet/610 m) and thermal imaging (2,000 feet/610 m).

  Speech: Full vocal capabilities but with a hissing, snarling, barely human sounding voice. Speaks, reads, and understands the common languages as well as over 30 pre-Rifts languages. Also speaks (but can not read) Dragonese and Splugorth at 80%, and Faerie Speak at 60%.

  Self-Destruct Program: To help make the Arch-Vampire appear to be something like the real thing, it does not explode when all the main body M.D.C. is destroyed, but rather bursts into flames. When the extremely intense blaze subsides, all that remains is ash.

7. Skill Programs: All standard Shemarrian skill programs, plus Lore: Demons & Monsters at 65%.

On Faerie Folk

Optional Source Material for Rifts® and Other RPGs

By Michael P. Yocom

Any attempt to catalog Faerie Folk is bound to be fraught with error. This is largely due to the multitude of "false Faeries," unrelated species that are mistakenly lumped into the Faerie category. In ancient times, humans had contact with a variety of species. As Earth's magic energy dwindled, this interaction also dwindled as creatures of magic began leaving for greener pastures, and random Rifts became less frequent, stranding fewer non-human mundane individuals on Earth. Over the centuries, inaccuracies began creeping into the stories of these ancient interactions. This was confounded by mass conversions to religions that didn't include belief in these beings, and then the growth of scientific inquiry, which found no evidence to support the stories, causing them to become relegated to archives of made-up stories and not treated with any deference.

With the Return of Magic, humans are once again having frequent contact with these interdimensional travelers. This makes it imperative to sort fact from fiction, and provide an accurate overview of the various Faeries and those species that were mistaken for Faeries in the past, or even continue to be mistaken for Faeries today. Descriptions of the more common types of Faeries – the Faeries, Pixies, Sprites, and so on – already exist, but there are a number of lesser-known Faeries and false Faeries that deserve mention.

Additional Faerie Folk

These are all relatively unknown beings that appear to be types of Faeries. They have the same instinctive magical abilities and they participate in the same kinds of activities as Faeries, and they possess Faerie Food, drink, and weapons. The Clurichaun and Far Darrig seem to be more closely related to Leprechauns than other Faeries, the Fenodyree seem to be related to Brownies and Grogach, and the Glaistig appears to be related to Pucks. It's unclear where the Gancanaugh and Korrigan fit within the Faerie family, but in it they definitely are.

bradshaw 2010

Clurichaun

Similar to, and often mistaken for, their cousins the Leprechauns, Clurichauns are less handsome, more surly, and have slightly different talents and obsessions. Like Leprechauns, Clurichauns are two to three feet (0.6 to 0.9 m) tall, have white hair, and are well-groomed and well-dressed. There the similarity ends, as Clurichauns have straight hair, and are balding and beardless. They also have large noses, ears, and chins. Their fashion sense is also somewhat more antiquated than Leprechauns: frocks, waistcoats, breeches, woolen stockings, riding boots, and bi- or tricorn hats, with a preference for blues and grays. Finally, Clurichauns almost never smile.

Their disposition is nothing like that of Leprechauns, being given towards grumpiness and even surliness. While Leprechauns value treasure above all else, even booze, Clurichauns only care about strong drink. They are preternatural cat burglars, and many a confused victim has woken up in the morning to find an entire wine cellar emptied, but not a single penny out of place.

Clurichauns hoard alcohol like Leprechauns hoard treasure, and their lairs are vast wine cellars, often accessible only through a magical maze. Their magic casks regenerate any drink poured into them, turning the relatively small quantities of stolen drink into endless founts of liquid joy. Many of the drinks will be enchanted in addition to highly intoxicating, and some will be traps: Faerie drinks and sleeping potions to make it easier to catch thieves. (These traps are never deadly.)

Despite their ability to create endless supplies of their drinks of choice, Clurichauns will never settle for just a few drops, and will always try to steal the entire bottle, keg, barrel, or even cask. This is because the magical regeneration produces the best results with at least a bottle's worth of starter stock, and any smaller starting stock will produce inferior results. They also refuse to surrender even a drop of their endless drink supply under any circumstances, and jealously guard their prized collections. (The exception being other Faerie Folk, with whom they will share drinks freely.)

No cheap swill for these diminutive connoisseurs, only the finest beverages are worthy of theft! Indeed, Clurichauns can even be coerced into using their skills to steal non-alcoholic items in exchange for an especially high-quality, rare drink. The would-be employer will need to be careful not to let the Clurichaun know where that choice beverage is stored prior to completion of the job, and must always pay up when the job is done, as Clurichauns exact terrible revenge when cheated.

Alignment: Almost always Miscreant (60%), Anarchist (25%), or Unprincipled (15%). However, even a selfish or evil Clurichaun will never deliberately hurt or betray another Faerie Folk.

Attributes: I.Q. 3D6, M.E. 2D6, M.A. 2D6, P.S. 2D6+2, P.P. 3D6+8, P.E. 3D6+4, P.B. 2D6, Spd 4D6 running.

M.D.C.: 1D6x20 on Rifts Earth. (Has P.E. number x6 for Hit Points, 5D6 S.D.C., and A.R. 8 in S.D.C. environments.)

P.P.E.: 1D6x100

R.C.C. Skills: Speak Faerie and Dragonese 98%, player characters can learn two additional Languages and Literacy in one at the base skill +30% skill bonus, Land Navigation 55%, Wilderness Survival 60%, Preserve Food 60%, Track Animals 40%, Faerie Lore 90%, Sing 60%, Dance 70%, Swim 80%, Prowl 40%, Climb 60%/50%, Concealment 60%, Pick Locks 75%, Locksmith 65%, Computer Operation 55%, Brewing 90%/95%, and Safe-Cracking 50%. Skills do not increase.

Horror Factor: 8

Size: Two to three feet tall (0.6 to 0.9 m).

Weight: 1D4x10 pounds (4.5-18 kg).

Natural Abilities: Nightvision 60 feet (18.3 m; can see in total darkness), keen normal vision, turn invisible at will, ventriloquism 88%, and sense secret compartments/doors 64% (automatic ability).

Magic: Escape, Chameleon, Charismatic Aura, Detect Concealment, Concealment, Reduce Self to Six Inches, Teleport: Superior.

Psionics: None.

Attacks per Melee: Five physical or two with magic.

Bonuses: +1 on initiative, +2 to parry and dodge, +2 to roll with impact, +3 to save vs magic, +2 to save vs Horror Factor.

Habitat: Like all Faeries, prefers wilderness, and lairs are usually located in remote areas, but most likely to be found within 100 miles (160 km) of cities or other potential sources of new drink stock.

Other Notes: Never wear armor. They don't trust most Big Folk, but are much more daring than Faeries in their dealings with humanoids. Most Clurichauns can out-drink the average human, consuming ten times their body weight before getting intoxicated! They consume so much booze that, despite this, they are always at least tipsy. Even drunk as a skunk, a Clurichaun is quick and cunning, and should be watched carefully.

Far Darrig

Another of the (larger) solitary Faerie Folk like Clurichauns and Leprechauns, Far Darrigs lack either of their cousins' obsessions (treasure or booze), but are obsessed with practical jokes. These odd creatures look like miniature Santa Clauses, being fat and bald with ruddy cheeks and long, white beards, and prone to dressing in red robes or suits with red caps. They find their coincidental resemblance to St. Nick to be greatly amusing, and often play the part if it furthers a prank. These jolly pranksters like to

46

wander all over the world, looking for unsuspecting mortals to play pranks on.

Although overly fond of playing pranks, especially on mortals, they seem to have a better understanding of their victims' limits than most Faerie Folk, and their pranks never put people in danger. Further, they never play pranks on children, other than possibly pretending to be Santa (complete with gifts of well-crafted toys), and will come to the aid of children if they are in need.

Alignment: Almost always Unprincipled (70%) or Anarchist (25%). However, even a selfish or evil Far Darrig will never deliberately hurt or betray another Faerie or a child of any species.

Attributes: I.Q. 3D6, M.E. 2D6+6, M.A. 3D6, P.S. 2D6+2, P.P. 3D6+6, P.E. 3D6, P.B. 2D6+4, Spd 4D6 running.

M.D.C.: 1D6x10 on Rifts Earth. (Has P.E. number x6 for Hit Points, 2D6 S.D.C. and A.R. 8 in S.D.C. environments.)

P.P.E.: 1D6x100

R.C.C. Skills: Speak Faerie and Dragonese 98%, player characters can learn two additional Languages and Literacy in one at the base skill +30% skill bonus, Land Navigation 55%, Wilderness Survival 60%, Preserve Food 60%, Track Animals 40%, Faerie Lore 90%, Sing 60%, Dance 70%, Swim 80%, Prowl 50%, Climb 60%/50%, Concealment 60%, Pick Locks 55%, Streetwise 54%, Art 60%, Whittling & Sculpting 55%, Carpentry 50%, and select two W.P.s of choice (any). Skills do not increase.

Horror Factor: 8

Size: Two to three feet tall (0.6 to 0.9 m).

Weight: 1D4x10+40 pounds (22.5-36 kg; tends to be roly-poly).

Natural Abilities: Nightvision 60 feet (18.3 m; can see in total darkness), keen normal vision, turn invisible at will, ventriloquism 88%, and sense secret compartments/doors 64% (automatic ability).

Magic: Escape, Chameleon, Charismatic Aura, Detect Concealment, Concealment, Reduce Self to Six Inches.

Psionics: None.

Attacks per Melee: Five physical or two with magic.

Bonuses: +1 on initiative, +1 to parry and dodge, +2 to roll with impact, +3 to save vs magic, +3 to save vs Horror Factor.

Habitat: Prefers wilderness like all Faeries.

Other Notes: Never wear armor. They don't trust most Big Folk, but are much more daring than Faeries in their dealings with humanoids. Most Far Darrigs can out-drink the average human, consuming four times their body weight before getting intoxicated! Even drunk as a skunk, a Far Darrig is quick and cunning, and should be watched carefully.

Fenodyree

Like the Brownie and Grogach, the Fenodyree (pronounced fenn ohd eh ree) is a small, extremely hairy, humanoid house spirit, who does domestic chores for a mortal family when no one is looking in exchange for gifts of food. Like the Grogach, they prefer to help out on farms, but prefer to perform chores in the farmhouse and barn, rather than the fields. They lack the muscular upper body of the Grogach, making them more closely resemble the Brownie, but their fur is red, rather than brown, and their feet are smaller. They have temperaments more like Brownies, being

bradshaw
2010

reclusive and not very mischievous (by Faerie standards). They do not engage in acts of revenge like the Grogach.

There is one noteworthy quirk of Fenodyrees: They view clothes as anti-hygienic, and will leave a farm if offered clothes – no matter how fancy – in payment for their services. As can be expected, this means that Fenodyrees are always naked, and never use any kind of armor. Despite this, one of the chores they frequently perform is to mend old clothes.

Alignment: Lean toward good; usually Principled (35%), Scrupulous (40%), or Unprincipled (20%).

Attributes: I.Q. 2D6, M.E. 2D6, M.A. 3D6, P.S. 2D6+1, P.P. 3D6, P.E. 3D6, P.B. 2D6+8, Spd 4D6 running.

M.D.C.: 6D6 + 24 on Rifts Earth. (Has P.E. x4 for Hit Points, 5D6 S.D.C. and an A.R. of 9 in S.D.C. settings.)

P.P.E.: 1D6x100

R.C.C. Skills: Skills do not increase.

Horror Factor: 8

Size: Two to three feet tall (0.6 to 0.9 m).

Weight: 2D4x10 pounds (9.1 to 36 kg).

Natural Abilities: Fly and hover in mid-air (even without wings; maximum height is 200 feet/61 m), nightvision 90 feet (27.4 m), see the invisible, keen normal vision and sense of smell, sense the location of crops and fruit trees 70%, sense location of secret compartments/doors 40%, and sense the location of ley lines 50%.

Magic: Mend Cloth, Mend Stone, Dowsing, Sleep, Animate Objects, Cure Minor Disorders, Repel Animals, Chameleon, and Purification.

Psionics: None.

Attacks per Melee: Four physical or two using magic.

Bonuses: +1 on initiative and +2 on all saving throws.

R.C.C. Skills: Speak Faerie and Gobblely 98%, player characters can learn two additional Languages at the base skill +20% skill bonus, Identify Plants and Fruits 75%, Brew 90/95%, Cook 80%, Preserve Food 80%, Recognize and Use Poison 70%, Holistic Medicine 55%, Gardening 80%, Land Navigation 90%, Wilderness Survival 90%, Sewing 60%, Faerie Lore 90%, Climb 70%/60%, Horsemanship: General 80%, and two W.P.s of choice. Skills do not increase.

Habitat: Most commonly found in farmhouses, ranch houses, and any outbuildings (barns, stables, bunkhouses, etc.). Less commonly found in wilderness areas among other Faerie Folk.

Other Notes: The only thing keeping Fenodyree from being as well-liked as Brownies by Big Folk is that they're relatively unknown and rare. They never wear body armor or clothes of any kind, and will abandon a homestead if given clothing. They seldom use any weapons except under the most dire of circumstances, such as self-defense, or protecting their adopted homestead or innocents in general.

Gancanaugh/Leanan Sídhe

The Gancanaugh (Male, pronounced "gahn cahn ah") and Leanan Sídhe (Female, pronounced "ley ahn ahn shee") – collectively known as the Faerie Lover – is a particularly dangerous type of Faerie. Small, purple, white-haired, and wingless, they normally spend their lives frolicking in the woods with other Faeries, playing pranks on Big Folk, and generally having fun. However, every once in a great while, a Faerie Lover will mysteriously develop an obsessive infatuation with a mortal!

Once this infatuation develops, an odd power manifests that is never known to be used any other time: the ability for the Faerie Lover to change its size to match that of the object of its affection, whether the mortal is small like a Dwarf or Gnome, Giant-sized, or somewhere in between. Everything else about the Faerie's appearance (skin, hair, and eye color, facial features, and so forth) remains unchanged. Since Faerie Lovers are universally very attractive, this doesn't really matter, and the mortal can often be seduced with ease.

The Faerie Lover proves to be a devoted, but not jealous or possessive mate, and a tender and adventurous lover. Further, prolonged exposure to the being's magical aura inspires great artistic talent in the mortal lover. If the mortal character already had artistic talent, it will be greatly enhanced; if not, an apparently latent talent will manifest. The talent can be any artistic expression: poetry, music, sculpture, painting, dance, acting, and so on. The character's works are so deeply touching that no one will be unmoved, and each viewer or listener who fails to save versus (non-Faerie) magic will be overwhelmed and left in tears.

The Faerie Lover will happily support and encourage these artistic talents, and use his or her charm to help with things like securing gallery showings and arranging meetings with potential patrons. All will seem to be roses for the happy couple, but

disaster is waiting in the wings. The Faerie Lover unknowingly secretes a drug-like toxin from his/her skin, which is easily absorbed by the mortal lover's skin. Once a month, the mortal lover will need to save versus poison, a failed roll meaning a nasty addiction sets in. Ironically, the drug boosts the mortal's artistic talent further, making subsequent works require a save versus Faerie Magic to avoid being overwhelmed.

The negative effects, however, are increasingly erratic behavior and development of an obsession with the Faerie Lover (the unknown source of the drug). Irrational suspicions of unfaithfulness, eventually developing into full-blown paranoia, set in, along with deepening insecurities about the character's own worth and questioning of whether or not he or she deserves the Faerie Lover.

Brilliant artistic works continue to be produced, but schedules begin to slip, the mortal lover begins to appear haggard, and public outbursts become common. The worried Faerie Lover will do what he or she can to help the mortal lover. (No one has discovered this biological quirk, so no antidotes are available.) A successful monthly save versus poison indicates remission, with the mortal waking up one day clear-headed, fully functional, and full of shame for the erratic and obsessive behavior of previous months.

These on-again, off-again periods of insanity get progressively worse – each episode picks up exactly where the last left off in terms of severity of irrational behavior, regardless of how many "good" months have passed in-between. A head is reached when paranoia finally sets in, with the mortal lover likely to do or say something abusive. Just like that, the Faerie Lover snaps out of his or her infatuation, reverts to natural size, and beats a hasty

bradshaw
2010

retreat. The Faerie will be briefly heartbroken before returning to normal Faerie pastimes. The mortal lover will experience a potentially fatal drug withdrawal.

The initial, dangerous period of withdrawal will last for one day per year the couple was together, regardless of frequency, intensity, or length of insanity periods. The character will be completely bed-ridden, unable to perform any actions, and will be wracked with hot and cold flashes, uncontrollable shaking, random flashes of intense pain, and occasional paralysis. For each day of withdrawal, there is an increasing chance of having a heart attack (10% on the first day, an additional 5% per additional day of withdrawal). Failure to resuscitate obviously means death. Characters who survive the initial withdrawal phase will be weak and lethargic, unable to get out of bed, for another 1D4 weeks, before returning more or less to normal.

The character has high (20%) chances of developing a phobia for Faerie Folk (curls up in a fetal position and cries like a baby at the sight of the tiniest, friendliest Faerie). If a phobia fails to emerge, there are equal odds of developing an obsession with Faerie Folk (will actively seek them out and happily accept being the butt of pranks, no matter how mean or dangerous). A reluctance to enter into future relationships is almost certain, and characters are likely to abandon artistic pursuits and refuse to ever witness their own works because of the memories they evoke.

Also known as: Purple Faerie, Faerie Lover.
Alignment: Overwhelmingly selfish; usually Unprincipled (25%), Anarchist (40%), or Miscreant (25%).
Attributes: I.Q. 2D6+6, M.E. 2D6, M.A. 3D6+12, P.S. 2D6, P.P. 3D6, P.E. 2D6+3, P.B. 2D6+12, Spd 4D6 running.
M.D.C.: 1D6x10+30 on Rifts Earth. (Has P.E. number x4 for Hit Points, 6D6 S.D.C. and A.R. 7 in S.D.C. environments.)
P.P.E.: 1D6x100
R.C.C. Skills: Speak Faerie and Dragonese 98%, player characters can learn two additional Languages and Literacy in one at the base skill +30% skill bonus, Cook 70%, Dance 60%, Sing 70%, Pick Locks 60%, Pick Pockets 50%, Holistic Medicine 40%, Climbing 80%/70%, Prowl 50%, Swimming 70%, Seduction 80%, Art 70%, Lore: Faerie 75%, Land Navigation 70%, Preserve Food 50%, Track Animals 40%, Wilderness Survival 60%, and two W.P.s of choice. Skills do not increase.
Horror Factor: 10
Size: Six inches tall (0.15 m) normally, anything from one to thirty feet tall (0.3 to 9.1 m) when attached to a mortal lover.
Weight: Six ounces (0.17 kg) normally, but weight adjusts with size.
Natural Abilities: Fly and hover, nightvision 90 feet (27.4 m; can see in total darkness), see the invisible, keen normal vision, sense the location of water 50%, sense the location of ley lines 80%, and locate secret compartments/doors 54%.
Size Change (special): The ability to change size to anything from Gnome- to Giant-sized. This ability is instinctive and outside the Faerie's ability to control. The size will be appropriate for the Faerie's current lover.
Magic: Befuddle, Charm, Love Charm, Sense Evil, Wind Rush, Tongues, and the Faeries' Dance (same as the Faeries' Circle, only it is a spell that lasts for 30 minutes or until cancelled by the Faerie spell caster).
Psionics: None.

Attacks per Melee: Four physical or two magical.
Bonuses: +2 to parry and dodge in flight, and +1 to save vs magic.
Habitat: Wilderness areas, normally in the company of other Faerie Folk. Faerie Lovers can rarely be encountered anywhere, and try to keep close to their mortal lovers.
Other Notes: None.

Glaistig

Members of this species are frequently mistaken for Satyrs or Pucks. Like these, the Glaistig (pronounced "glash tig") is a humanoid with goat-like legs. Contrary to what ancient legends claim, Glaistig do come in both male and female form, but only one in every twenty Glaistig is male. Regardless of the sex, the Glaistig is an attractive, albeit somewhat small humanoid with hairy, goat-like legs.

They generally hide their goat legs beneath dresses or robes, with a strong preference for green cloth. Glaistig females lure humans back to their lairs, where they keep them prisoner. A harem of ten to forty human slaves is kept docile through Faerie Magic, and once a week the Glaistig will feast on her slaves by cutting each one and draining a few points of P.P.E.

Glaistig males wander instead of building lairs, adding to the idea that they don't exist, since missing girls are chalked up to runaways or bandits. They keep a smaller group of humanoid slaves (two to eight) and subsist mostly by nightly visits to local girls as they pass through a village, leaving a wake of girls confused by the especially intense, erotic "dreams" they had and a cut or two that weren't there at bedtime.

Alignment: Lean towards evil; mostly Miscreant (60%) and Diabolic (30%). Regardless of alignment, the Glaistig is loyal and dedicated to its harem of human slaves/food, and will fight to the death to protect any of its slaves.

Attributes: I.Q. 3D6, M.E. 2D6+3, M.A. 2D6+6, P.S. 2D6, P.P. 3D6, P.E. 3D6, P.B. 2D6+8, Spd 4D6.

M.D.C.: 1D6x10+60 on Rifts Earth. (Has P.E. x5 for Hit Points, 1D4x10 S.D.C. and A.R. 10 in S.D.C. worlds.)

P.P.E.: 1D6x100

R.C.C. Skills: Speaks Faerie and Gobblely 98%, player characters can learn two additional Languages at the base skill +10% skill bonus, NPCs will know one or two local Languages at 80%, Land Navigation 70%, Wilderness Survival 75%, Track Animals 60%, Track Humans 80%, Faerie Lore 85%, Demon & Monster Lore 70%, Dance 75%, Prowl 50%, Concealment 48%, Pick Locks 65%, Streetwise 48%, Climb 90%/80%, Swim 80%, and select two Piloting skills and five W.P.s (any) of choice. Skills do not increase.

Horror Factor: 10

Size: Three to four feet tall (0.9 to 1.2 m).

Weight: 3D6+60 pounds (28 to 35 kg).

Natural Abilities: Nightvision 90 feet (27.4 m), excellent normal vision, sense the location of water 50%, sense the location of ley lines 50%, and metamorphosis into a goat.

Magic: Blind, Charm, Cure Minor Disorders, Invisibility (Superior), Light Healing, Reduce Self (6 inches).

Feeding (special): The Glaistig is a P.P.E. vampire, similar to the Psi-Stalker, except the Glaistig can feed on any living, intelligent being (not just psychics, practitioners of magic, or supernatural creatures), but can only drain a few points of P.P.E. at a time per victim. Glaistig feed in a manner similar to the Psi-Stalker's non-lethal feeding, cutting the victim and remotely draining 2D6 points of P.P.E. (not to exceed the victim's available P.P.E.). The Glaistig can only feed on a given victim once per week, and requires 60 P.P.E. per week. The Glaistig cannot gorge, and becomes weak without a steady supply of P.P.E. (Reduce skills and spell durations by half, and eliminate bonuses, any time the Glaistig drops below 60 P.P.E. consumed in the last week.)

Forget (special): The Glaistig has the ability to magically induce a victim to believe that the memories of a feeding were nothing more than a dream. This power is most often used by male Glaistig, but down-on-their-luck females who currently don't have an established lair or harem will use it, as well.

Psionics: None.

Attacks per Melee: Six physical attacks or two using magic.

Bonuses: +3 on initiative, +2 to strike, parry, and dodge, +2 to roll with impact, +3 to save vs Horror Factor, +3 on all saving throws.

Habitat: Females build lairs in wilderness areas near a village or small town. Males can be encountered anywhere.

Other Notes: None.

Korrigan

Korrigans are small, beautiful females with pale complexions, black hair, and glowing, red eyes. They are fond of singing and dancing. Incorrigible flirts, they like to lead mortal males on, milking endless streams of compliments, gifts, and dancing from love-struck unfortunates, even pitting two or more suitors against each other in non-violent competitions such as poetry recitals, foot races, riddle competitions, and the like. (Korrigans abhor violence.) One day, without warning, the Korrigan is simply gone, having gotten bored with her suitors and moved on to greener pastures.

Alignment: Almost all are Anarchist (50%) or Miscreant (40%).

Attributes: I.Q. 2D6, M.E. 2D6, M.A. 3D6, P.S. 2D6, P.P. 4D6, P.E. 2D6+4, P.B. 2D6+6, Spd 4D6 running.

M.D.C.: 1D6x10+60 on Rifts Earth. (Has P.E. number x3 for Hit Points, 1D4x10+10 S.D.C. and A.R. 10 in S.D.C. environments.)

P.P.E.: 1D6x100

R.C.C. Skills: Skills do not increase.

Horror Factor: 10

Size: Four to five feet tall (1.2 to 1.5 m).

Weight: 1D4x10+60 pounds (32 to 45 kg).

Natural Abilities: Fly and hover, nightvision 90 feet (27.4 m), keen normal vision, turn invisible at will, and sense the location of ley lines 50%.

Magic: Charm, Sleep, Wind Rush, Globe of Daylight, Tongues, Chameleon, Metamorphosis: Animal, Influence the Beast.

Psionics: None.

Attacks per Melee: Four physical or two using magic.

Bonuses: +1 on initiative, +2 to strike, +3 to save vs all types of Nature Magic (Spoiling, Shamanism, etc.), +1 to save vs all other types of magic and poison, +2 to save vs Horror Factor.

Habitat: Wilderness areas with a preference for roadsides or any other place she can readily find admirers without having to deal with crowds of mortals.

Other Notes: None.

Faerie Animals

These odd beings are animals that appear to be related to Faeries somehow. They don't use Faerie artifacts (food, drink, and weapons), but do have some of the instinctive powers of Faeries. They also show a strong affinity for Faeries, coming to the aid of any Faerie in trouble they encounter, and vice versa.

Alp-Luachra

The Alp-Luachra is a tiny, newt-like parasite with a handful of instinctive magical powers. These strange creatures live near streams, and when a humanoid takes a nap near the stream, the Alp-Luachra climbs into his stomach through his mouth. Once in place, the creature begins excreting a slimy substance that protects it from stomach acid, and steals some of the host's food. The excreted substance generally affects its host as a deliriant, a special class of hallucinogenic which causes complete separation from reality.

The Alp-Luachra produces its antacid slime in spurts, coating itself and then letting the coating break down before replenishing it with another spurt. This causes the host to experience cyclical hallucination episodes as the amount of deliriant entering the bloodstream waxes and wanes. The frequency of episodes depends largely on stomach acidity, and ranges from two to eight weeks between episodes. (2D4 weeks, less if a worrier or frequent consumer of acid drinks like coffee or spicy food, more if the host himself regularly consumes antacids.)

During an episode, the host will be completely confused. One common effect is that the host believes he is holding a conversation with someone, when the room is actually empty. Another effect is that he will be unable to recognize acquaintances, even himself in a mirror, often leading to him getting angry at the stranger he thinks is mimicking him. The host will also be left with false memories of the period, and the entire experience is highly unpleasant.

The Alp-Luachra slime is also highly toxic, with each episode accompanied by an additional 1% chance, beginning at 1% with the first episode, of renal (kidney) failure. (The average frequency between episodes is four weeks, so each episode has a better than 50/50 chance of causing renal failure after a little less than four years.) Renal failure requires the host undergo dialysis or face death, but the kidneys will return to normal three to six months after the parasite is removed.

The parasite clings to the stomach lining, so vomiting won't get rid of it, and is highly resistant to toxins, such as those in anti-parasite medications. The only way to get rid of an Alp-Luachra besides surgery is to ingest large amounts of salty food without water. The tiny amphibian is easily dehydrated, and will leave if the environment is perceived to be too dry. This is aided by taking another streamside nap, as the parasite can sense nearby bodies of water and will crawl back out the mouth and hop into the stream.

Although less frequently encountered in the company of Faerie Folk than other Faerie Animals, Alp-Luachras are sometimes kept as pets by Faeries. They are the only Faerie Animal too small to be used as a riding animal by Faeries.

Alignment: Essentially Anarchist.

Attributes: I.Q. Low Animal Intelligence, M.E. 1D6, M.A. 1D6, P.S. 1D6, P.P. 2D6+12, P.E. 2D6+6, P.B. 3D6+6, Spd 3D6+6.

M.D.C.: 1D6 on Rifts Earth (Has 1D6 Hit Points and 1D6 S.D.C. in S.D.C. environments.)

P.P.E.: 1D6x100

Physical Appearance: Looks like a normal newt with a brownish-red body and yellow banded stripes.

Size: 3-6 inches (7.6-15 cm).

Weight: 2-3 ounces (57-85 g).

Average Life Span: 150-200 years.

Natural Abilities: Prowl 90%, highly toxic skin secretions, sense water within a 10 mile (16 km) radius, turn invisible at will.

Magic: Blinding Flash, Befuddle, Blind, Repel Animals. These are cast instinctively on attackers and predators, not consciously nor strategically.

Psionics: None.

Attacks per Melee: None against humanoids except by magic. Has two melee actions or one spell per round.

Bonuses: +2 to dodge.

Habitat: Bodies of fresh water, especially streams.

bradshaw
2010

Arkan Sonney

In Pre-Rifts days, this hedgehog-like creature was known to the inhabitants of the Isle of Man. Generally considered a type of magical or "Faerie" animal, the Arkan Sonney was believed to bring luck to anyone who caught one. (No mean feat, considering their size-changing powers make it extremely difficult to catch them.) Although they are actually of dubious use as charms, since a captive Arkan Sonney attracts Faerie rescuers, they do possess a range of magical powers normally associated with Faerie Folk, including the aforementioned size-changing, a kind of limited metamorphosis.

This and their affinity for Faerie Folk are often cited as evidence that Arkan Sonneys, like the Cat Sìth and Cu Sìth (and, sometimes, Alp-Luachra), are Faerie Animals and, further, for the existence of the Faerie Realm, the hypothetical home dimension of Faeries, on the assumption that a variety of Faerie species, including animals, have to have evolved in a common environment.

Arkan Sonneys appear like albino hedgehogs, having white fur and spines, and pink eyes, but their ears are also bright red. Like normal hedgehogs, they are nocturnal insectivores who sleep most of the day in small burrows, who bite and lick sources of new smells, then "anoint" themselves with the scented froth that results as a kind of scent camouflage, and roll into spiny balls when threatened. Being pricked by an Arkan Sonney spine causes the effects of certain Faerie Foods and Drinks. Their apparently enchanted spines and their size-changing abilities are their only magical abilities, being unintelligent animals.

They are sometimes seen being used as riding animals by wingless Faeries, and all Faeries seem to be immune to the enchanted spines. They are occasionally hunted (for capture) by mortals seeking luck, despite considerable evidence that they not only don't provide luck to their owners, but attract extra mischief and even attacks from Faeries. Splynncryth's minions have, unfortunately, recently discovered that the enchanted spines continue to be effective even after death, and consuming raw Arkan Sonney meat temporarily grants the size-changing and a few (1D4) spine powers, making them attractive for horrific Bio-Wizard experimentation.

Faerie Folk are highly protective of the Arkan Sonney, as if they were prized pets or even friends despite their animal levels of intelligence. A mortal who rescues an Arkan Sonney, particularly from supernatural monsters known to hunt the "fairy hedgehog" for its meat, can expect to gain the friendship of the Faerie Folk.

Alignment: Essentially Anarchist.
Attributes: I.Q. Low Animal Intelligence, M.E. 2D4, M.A. 1D6+4, P.S. 2D4, P.P. 2D6+6, P.E. 3D6, P.B. 3D6, Spd 2D6+12.
M.D.C.: 2D6 on Rifts Earth. (Has 2D4 Hit Points and 2D4 S.D.C. in S.D.C. environments.)
P.P.E.: 1D6x100
Physical Appearance: Looks like an albino, but otherwise normal, hedgehog, except for its bright red ears.
Size: 8-12 inches (20-30 cm) in length.
Weight: Up to 3.5 pounds (1.6 kg).
Average Life Span: 200-300 years.
Natural Abilities: Prowl 80%, scent camouflage (anything trying to track an Arkan Sonney by scent is -20% to do so), turn invisible at will.
Magic: No spell casting abilities, but the Arkan Sonney does have two potent, magical abilities.
  Quills (special): Anything pricked by a quill (1 point S.D.C. or M.D.C. damage as appropriate) that fails to save vs Faerie Magic will suffer the same effects as a random item of Faerie Food (roll percentiles):
  01-02 Acorn Nuts.
  03-05 Beef Cake.
  06-08 Beetle Nuts.
  09-11 Beets.
  12-14 Blossom Wine.
  15-17 Bubbly Wine.
  18-20 Burgundy Wine.
  21-22 Cauliflower.
  23-25 Candy Walnut.
  26-28 Candy Almond.
  29-31 Cinnamon Sticks.
  32-34 Coffee.
  35-37 Cookoo Eggs.
  38-40 Cordial.
  41-42 Duck.
  43-45 Faerie Ointment.
  46-48 Flounder.
  49-51 Frog's Legs.
  52-54 Goose.
  55-57 Green Beans.
  58-60 Magic Mushrooms.
  61-62 Mixed Nuts.
  63-65 Mushroom Saute.
  66-68 Mushroom Tonic.
  69-71 Mussels.
  72-74 Peanuts.
  75-77 Pears.
  78-80 Pigeon Roast.
  81-82 Red Wine.
  83-85 Skunk Cabbage.
  86-88 Sloe Wine.
  89-91 Squash.

92-94 Tomatoes.
95-97 Turkey.
98-00 Tarts.

Trying to grab an Arkan Sonney that has curled into a ball results in multiple quill pricks. (2D6 S.D.C./M.D. and an equal number of Faerie Food effects: roll or select from the list above.) Armored gloves will absorb the damage, but the magical effects pass through to the wearer.

Size Change (special): This is a limited form of metamorphosis that allows the Arkan Sonney to change size at will to anything from as small as an ant to as large as a calf, which makes it extremely difficult to keep an Arkan Sonney captive. This power can be used up to three times daily. The Arkan Sonney can return to natural size at any time.

Psionics: None.

Attacks per Melee: None against humanoids except by magic. Has two melee actions per round. Quills are an entirely passive defense and pricking with them does not count as an action.

Bonuses: +1 to dodge.

Habitat: Prefers forested wildernesses, but can occasionally be encountered above the tree line or in grasslands.

Cat Sìth

The Cat Sìth (pronounced "kett shee"), or "Faerie Cat," has an undeservedly evil reputation, being described since Medieval times as transformed witches, the familiars of witches, or spectral omens of death. In reality, these large cats belong to the Faerie Animals, a handful of animal species who possess some of the powers peculiar to Faeries, as well as a kind of mutual affinity, often seeking each other's company and coming to each other's aid.

Cat Sìth are similar in appearance to domestic cats, albeit quite a bit larger. They are mostly black with white chests, and their large size, black color, and limited magical abilities probably all contributed to acquiring a bad reputation in the Middle Ages.

Like domestic cats and related Wildcat subspecies, Cat Sìth hunt small mammals, birds, and lizards. They are, however, diurnal, being most active during the day. Like the other Faerie Animals, they sometimes serve as steeds for wingless Fairies.

Alignment: Essentially Anarchist.

Attributes: I.Q. High Animal Intelligence, M.E. 2D6, M.A. 2D4, P.S. 2D6, P.P. 2D6+12, P.E. 3D6, P.B. 3D6, Spd 2D6+6.

M.D.C.: 3D6 on Rifts Earth. (Has 2D6 Hit Points and 2D6 S.D.C. in S.D.C. environments.)

P.P.E.: 1D6x100

Physical Appearance: Large, black cat with white undersides.

Size: 23-25 inch (58-63 cm) body length, plus a 13-19 inch (33-48 cm) tail.

Weight: 9-23 pounds (4-10 kg).

Average Life Span: 400-500 years.

Natural Abilities: Keen vision and sense of smell, nightvision 100 feet (30 m), Prowl 90%, Climb 80%, Swim 60%, can leap 5 feet (1.5 m) high and 6 feet (1.8 m) long, turn invisible at will.

Magic: Befuddle, Paralysis: Lesser, See the Invisible. These are cast instinctively on attackers and prey, not consciously nor strategically.

Fear (special): The same effects as the Fear invocation, but the area of fear is centered on the Cat Sìth. Like its other magical powers, this is not a spell in the traditional sense as it is cast reflexively, as part of the feline intimidation reaction to threats. Like domestic cats, Cat Sìth arch their backs, bristle their fur, and hiss when threatened, but also cast this modified Fear spell.

Bite of Fury (special): The same effects as the Fist of Fury spell, but cast on the Cat Sìth's mouth, instead of a paw, enabling the fairy cat to inflict Mega-Damage bites as if it had Supernatural Strength. This is cast instinctively when hunting or fighting supernatural prey.

Psionics: None.

Attacks per Melee: Four physical or two using magic.

Bonuses: +2 on initiative, +3 to strike, +2 to parry, +3 to dodge, +3 to save vs Horror Factor.

Habitat: Prefers dense, temperate forests and can be found most commonly in magic-rich, forested wildernesses. On Rifts Earth, they are most common in the eastern United States except for Florida and the Gulf Coast, all across Canada and Alaska, and across Siberia and Europe.

Cu Sìth

The Cu Sìth (pronounced "koo shee"), or "Faerie Dog," is a very large canine, although ancient stories exaggerate the size somewhat. Described as being as big as a cow or large calf, this powerfully-built canine is actually more the weight of an English Mastiff or Puma, and with dimensions similar to that of the English Mastiff (rather than the long and slender Puma). Not an actual "dog" in the sense of being related to domestic dogs, the Cu Sìth looks more like a large, green fox than a dog or wolf.

Like other Faerie Animals, the Cu Sìth possesses limited, instinctive magical abilities and frequently associates with Faerie Folk, seeming to be both a pet and occasional riding animal. Due to its large size, it can be ridden by several Faeries at once.

Alignment: Essentially Anarchist.

Attributes: I.Q. High Animal Intelligence, M.E. 2D6, M.A. 2D6, P.S. 2D6+6, P.P. 2D6, P.E. 3D6+6, P.B. 3D6, Spd 2D6.

M.D.C.: 1D4x10 on Rifts Earth. (Has 4D6+10 Hit Points and 2D6+20 S.D.C. in S.D.C. environments.)

P.P.E.: 1D6x100

Physical Appearance: Large, green, fox-like canine.

Size: 28-37 inches (71-94 cm) tall, 75-98 inches (190-249 cm) long.

Weight: 120-250 pounds (54-113 kg).

Average Life Span: 600-750 years.

Natural Abilities: Keen vision and sense of smell, nightvision 60 feet (18 m), prowl 75%, swim 65%, track by smell 55%, leap 3 feet (0.9 m) high and 5 feet (1.5 m) long, turn invisible at will.

Magic: Befuddle, Paralysis: Lesser, See the Invisible. These are cast instinctively on attackers and prey, not consciously nor strategically.

Bite of Fury (special): The same effects as the Fist of Fury spell, but cast on the Cu Sith's mouth, instead of a paw, enabling the Faerie Dog to inflict Mega-Damage bites as if it had Supernatural Strength. This is cast instinctively when hunting or fighting supernatural prey.

Psionics: None.

Attacks per Melee: Four physical or two using magic.

Bonuses: +2 on initiative, +3 to strike, +4 to dodge, +2 to save vs Horror Factor.

Habitat: Prefers dense, temperate forests and can be found most commonly in magic-rich, forested wildernesses. On Rifts Earth, they are most common in the eastern United States except for Florida and the Gulf Coast, all across Canada and Alaska, and across Siberia and Europe.

False Faerie Folk

Throughout the centuries, various species have been mistakenly classified as Faeries. Not every diminutive humanoid or magical being is a Faerie! Following are some of the lesser-known species that frequently get confused with Faeries.

The Bean Nighe and Caoineag appear to be related to the Banshee in some ways (the Banshee itself being mistaken for Faeries in the past; the word itself even derives from the Irish Gaelic "Bean Sídhe," literally "Faerie Woman"). The Coblynau, Knocker, and possibly Pech appear to form a genus of closely-related species with Gnomes, rather than the Faeries. The Lutin does appear to be distantly related to Faeries, in much the same way Goblins are.

Bean Nighe

Much like the similar Banshee, the Bean Nighe ("Washer Woman") was mistaken for a type of Faerie in ancient times. Like the Banshee, the Bean Nighe is actually an ethereal P.P.E. scavenger with the ability to detect the likelihood of death. However, unlike the Banshee, the Bean Nighe does not just wait around passively. Instead, the fiend uses its several psionic powers to tip the balance, suppressing the victim's morale and making him slip up at critical moments. These pathetic creatures are not intelligent enough to realize that the other guy in the fight could just as easily be a food source, and obsessively try to tip the balance against their current target.

Alignment: Miscreant.

Attributes: I.Q. 2D6+4, M.E. 1D6, M.A. 1D6, P.S. 1D6, P.P. 3D6, P.E. 1D6, P.B. 1D6, Spd 4D6.

Hit Points: 50. Like the undead, Bean Nighes are impervious to most man-made weapons, and are vulnerable only to psionics and magic, including magic weapons and Techno-Wizard weapons that fire TK rounds or magical bolts of energy.

S.D.C.: 50

P.P.E.: 2D6+2

R.C.C. Skills: None, animal-like predator.

Horror Factor: 14

Size: 6-10 feet tall (1.8-3 m) and has no measurable weight in its spirit form.

Average Life Span: Immortal until slain.

Natural Abilities: Ethereal, which means it can walk through solid matter, like walls, while physical attacks, like bullets, fire, and energy blasts, do no damage (pass right through it). Hovers and floats above the ground up to 100 feet (30.5 m) high. Teleport self only, up to 2,000 miles (3,200 km), but only when going to a new feeding site. Natural state is invisible and it cannot make itself visible. Natural Empathy: Automatically senses emotions as well as sickness and death (costs no I.S.P.). Natural Empathic Transmission of Sorrow: Radiates in a 60 foot (18.3 m) radius around the Bean Nighe, costs no I.S.P. (automatic); mortals save as normal vs psionic attack from sorrow/despair. Also see psionics.

Magic: None.

Psionics: I.S.P.: 100. Clairvoyance (4), Empathic Transmission (6), Empathy (4), Psychic Diagnosis (4), Sense Magic (3). Equal to 5th level strength. Considered a Major Psychic.

Enemies: None, per se.

Allies: None, per se.

Attacks per Melee: Three hand to hand attacks with Astral Travelers only.

Bonuses: None; it's a scavenger and psychic carrion feeder.

Habitat: Can be encountered anywhere that death is imminent.

Caoineag

Another ethereal P.P.E. scavenger mistaken for a Faerie in ancient times, the Caoineag ("Weeper") differs from the Banshee and Bean Nighe in that it can only feed on the P.P.E. emitted at the moment of death by a being of evil alignment (Aberrant, Miscreant, or Diabolic). Like the Bean Nighe, the Caoineag takes an active role in ensuring the probable death it senses, but with a different approach. Whereas the Bean Nighe trips up the victim, the Caoineag seeks out nearby champions of good, temporarily aiding them by giving them information in their dreams, leading them to helpful items or potential allies via disembodied singing, and warning them of traps and ambushes with the wailing typical of this group of death spirits.

Alignment: Principled.

Attributes: I.Q. 3D6, M.E. 2D4, M.A. 2D6, P.S. 1D6, P.P. 3D6, P.E. 1D6, P.B. 2D4, Spd 4D6.

Hit Points: 50. Like the undead, Caoineag are impervious to most man-made weapons, and are vulnerable only to psionics and magic, including magic weapons and Techno-Wizard weapons that fire TK rounds or magical bolts of energy.

S.D.C.: 50

P.P.E.: 3D6

R.C.C. Skills: None, animal-like predator.

Horror Factor: 14

Size: 6-10 feet tall (1.8-3 m) and has no measurable weight in its spirit form.

Average Life Span: Immortal until slain.

Natural Abilities: Ethereal, which means it can walk through solid matter, like walls, while physical attacks, like bullets, fire, and energy blasts, do no damage (pass right through it). Hovers and floats above the ground up to 100 feet (30.5 m) high. Teleport self only, up to 2,000 miles (3,200 km), but only when going to a new feeding site. Natural state is invisible and it cannot make itself visible. Natural Empathy: Automatically senses emotions as well as sickness and death (costs no I.S.P.). Natural Empathic Transmission of Sorrow: Radiates in a 60 foot (18.3 m) radius around the Caoineag, costs no I.S.P. (automatic); mortals save as normal vs psionic attack from sorrow/despair. Also see psionics.

Magic: None.

Psionics: I.S.P.: 100. Clairvoyance (4), Empathy (4), Psychic Diagnosis (4), Sense Magic (3).

Dream Visions (special)

Range: 250 feet (76 m) per level of experience.

Duration: 20 minutes.

I.S.P.: 16

Saving Throw: None as the target is asleep.

This is the ability to direct the target's dreams with the intention of communication. Communication is muddled as every mind (even those of the same species) operates differently, and the target will need to decipher the meaning of the dream

imagery once awake. The target will know that the dream is special and is guaranteed to remember it on waking.

Ethereal Singing (special)
    Range: 1.5 miles (2.4 km).
    Duration: 10 minutes per level of experience.
    I.S.P.: 10
    Ethereal Singing causes haunting, otherworldly music to be emitted from the psychic's current location. The "voice" heard has nothing to do with the psychic's regular voice, and normal speech is unaffected. This ability is meant primarily to attract people to a specific spot, although it can scare away the superstitious.

Enemies: None, per se.
Allies: None, per se.
Attacks per Melee: Three hand to hand attacks with Astral Travelers only.
Bonuses: None; it's a scavenger and psychic carrion feeder.
Habitat: Can be encountered anywhere an evil being's death is imminent, but is much rarer than the Banshee and Bean Nighe. Typically stalk evil beings with especially high levels of P.P.E.

Coblynau

These diminutive, subterranean beings resemble, and may be cousins to, the Gnomes. They are blind in what humans know as the visible portion of the electromagnetic spectrum, instead seeing in long-wavelength infrared, the range emitted by cool objects. As such, the walls of pitch black mine tunnels appear to glow to Coblynau, allowing them to find their way underground without lights. Warm-blooded animals (most humanoids included) glow brightly to Coblynau, making it impossible to hide from them.

The downside to this ability is that they absolutely hate the surface in daytime, as everything glows brightly, hurting their eyes. As such, they will insist on only traveling at night.

They are secretive and territorial, living in underground cities of low-ceilinged tunnels and chambers. Their reputation for causing cave-ins in mines is well earned, as blundering surface dwellers, ignorant of the presence of a Coblynau city, wreak havoc digging mine tunnels, earning the ire of the Coblynau.

Alignment: Any, but most are Miscreant or Aberrant.
Attributes: I.Q. 3D6, M.E. 1D6+6, M.A. 3D6, P.S. 1D6, P.P. 4D6, P.E. 3D6+6, P.B. 4D6, Spd 2D6 running, 1D6 digging.
Hit Points: P.E. +1D6 per level of experience.
S.D.C.: Standard.
P.P.E.: 4D6
O.C.C. Skill Notes: Add +10% to Prowl and +5% to any of the following: Surveillance, Intelligence, General Repair, Masonry, Carpentry, Rope Works, Locate Secret Compartments/Doors, and Land Navigation.
Horror Factor: None.
Physical Appearance: Similar to Gnomes, but slightly smaller and with black hair and gray skin. Short, thin, handsome people with bushy eyebrows and sparkling eyes. Males almost always sport a neatly trimmed beard and/or mustache. Females generally have long, flowing hair and look like beautiful porcelain dolls brought to life.
Size: 16-20 inches (41-51 cm) tall.

Weight: 10-20 pounds (4.5-9 kg).
Average Life Span: 300+ years.
Natural Abilities:

Infrared Vision (special): Everything with a temperature in the range 32-132° F (0-56° C) emits radiation in the range visible to the character, essentially glowing. The exact frequency emitted is also linked to temperature, so the character can also make a fair estimate of the temperature of an object based on what "color" it glows. Since the character's eyes see a completely different portion of the EM spectrum, he has a completely different concept of color. "Blue," "orange," and "chartreuse" are meaningless words, and beautiful paintings will look flat unless the pigments also absorb and reflect differently from each other in the infrared. Conversely, things that look monotone to others may have visible variation to the character – such as a flat, gray wall with a hot spot.

Underground Tunneling (special): Can build solid, strong tunnels (no fear of a cave-in) with great speed and dexterity. They can also excavate ruins and the sites of cave-ins with the same prowess. In addition, the character can usually tell if an existing tunnel or chamber is a natural formation or whether it was dug by Gnomes, Dwarves, Kobolds, Goblins, Troglodytes, or humans. The character can even tell if it's new, old, or ancient. **Base Skill:** 30% +5% per level of experience.

Underground Architecture: Coblynau, like Gnomes, are competent underground architects. Likewise, the character can recognize the styles of Gnome (Coblynau do have a different architectural style from Gnomes and Knockers), Dwarf, Kobold, Goblin, and other types of construction. The Coblynau

who is traveling slowly and cautiously, looking for traps, can locate them, and avoid or deactivate them. **Base Skill:** 20% +5% per level of experience; detection and deactivation of traps is done at half his normal architectural skill level.

Underground Sense of Direction: The character has an innate ability to tell direction when underground, even when blinded (not applicable on the surface). Thus, the Coblynau can tell whether he is traveling up, down, or level, the approximate angle of decline or ascent, approximately how far below the surface he is, and the approximate direction (north, south, east, or west). **Base Skill:** 30% +5% per level of experience.

This skill also enables him to judge the approximate location of surface structures (natural and artificial), but only if the character is familiar with the area. The character will also recognize traits and aspects of the underground tunnel or construct that serve as landmarks for him. **Base Skill:** 20% +5% per level of experience; -20% if in an unfamiliar area.

Magic: Per O.C.C.
Psionics: None.
Enemies: All non-Coblynau! Highly xenophobic. Characters forced to associate with other species will be belligerent and aloof at the best of times.
Allies: Other Coblynau, even those from other nations.
Attacks per Melee: Standard.
Bonuses: +1 to save vs poison and disease.
Habitat: Prefer mountainous areas, especially regions with steep-sided, narrow canyons. On Rifts Earth they can occasionally be encountered in the Rockies, Andes, Alps, and Himalayas. They are exceedingly rare on the Palladium World, but can be

found in the Old Kingdom Mountains and the Great Northern Mountains, with a number of populous, as yet undiscovered, kingdoms in the Yin-Sloth Jungles.

Favorite Weapons: Any weapon small enough to be used.

Other Notes: Like Gnomes, Coblynau have difficulty finding clothing, armor, weapons, and tools that are small enough for them (when outside their own kingdoms). They can use Gnome-sized weapons normally (half the damage of human-sized weapons), or can use human-sized weapons with penalties of -6 to strike and parry, and -6 to dodge if the weapon is heavier than a knife or dagger.

Knocker

Knockers are diminutive, subterranean humanoids. Like their cousins the Coblynau, Knockers look like Gnomes, and see in long-wavelength infrared, rather than human-visible light. Unlike Coblynau, Knockers are dark green, are not especially territorial, and are mute, communicating completely via Telepathy.

Whereas Coblynau build secret, underground cities, Knockers seek out existing mines, and build their tunnels off these. The entrances to their tunnels are extremely well-hidden. Despite their secretive and reclusive nature, they are helpful, using their natural psionic abilities to detect impending cave-ins and warn miners with knocking noises at the danger site.

Alignment: Any, but lean towards Principled, Scrupulous, or Unprincipled.

Attributes: I.Q. 3D6, M.E. 1D6+6, M.A. 2D6+6, P.S. 1D6+6, P.P. 4D6, P.E. 3D6+6, P.B. 4D6, Spd 2D6 running, 1D6 digging.

Hit Points: P.E. +1D6 per level of experience.

S.D.C.: Standard.

P.P.E.: 4D6

O.C.C. Skill Notes: Add +10% to Prowl and +5% to any of the following: Surveillance, Intelligence, General Repair, Masonry, Carpentry, Rope Works, Locate Secret Compartments/ Doors, and Land Navigation.

Horror Factor: None.

Physical Appearance: Similar to Gnomes, but dark green in complexion and with black hair.

Size: 2.5-3 feet (0.76-0.91 m) tall.

Weight: 30-70 pounds (14-31.5 kg).

Average Life Span: 300+ years.

Natural Abilities:

Infrared vision (special): Everything with a temperature in the range 32-132° F (0-56° C) emits radiation in the range visible to the character, essentially glowing. The exact frequency emitted is also linked to temperature, so the character can also make a fair estimate of temperature of an object based on what "color" it glows. Since the character's eyes see a completely different portion of the EM spectrum, he has a completely different concept of color. "Blue," "orange," and "chartreuse" are meaningless words, and beautiful paintings will look flat unless the pigments also absorb and reflect differently from each other in the infrared. Conversely, things that look monotone to

others may have visible variation to the character – such as a flat, gray wall with a hot spot.

Underground Tunneling (special): Can build solid, strong tunnels (no fear of a cave-in) with great speed and dexterity. They can also excavate ruins and the sites of cave-ins with the same prowess. In addition, the character can usually tell if an existing tunnel or chamber is a natural formation or whether it was dug by Gnomes, Dwarves, Kobolds, Goblins, Troglodytes, or humans. The character can even tell if it's new, old, or ancient. **Base Skill:** 30% +5% per level of experience.

Underground Architecture: Knockers, like Gnomes, are competent underground architects. Likewise, the character can recognize the styles of Gnome (Knockers do have a different architectural style from Gnomes and Coblynau), Dwarf, Kobold, Goblin, and other types of construction. The Knocker who is traveling slowly and cautiously, looking for traps, can locate them, and avoid or deactivate them. **Base Skill:** 20% +5% per level of experience; detection and deactivation of traps is done at half his normal architectural skill level.

Underground Sense of Direction: The character has an innate ability to tell direction when underground, even when blinded (not applicable on the surface). Thus, the Knocker can tell whether he is traveling up, down, or level, the approximate angle of decline or ascent, approximately how far below the surface he is, and the approximate direction (north, south, east, or west). **Base Skill:** 30% +5% per level of experience.

This skill also enables him to judge the approximate location of surface structures (natural and artificial), but only if the character is familiar with the area. The character will also recognize traits and aspects of the underground tunnel or construct that serve as landmarks for him. **Base Skill:** 20% +5% per level of experience; -20% if in an unfamiliar area.

Magic: Per O.C.C.

Psionics: I.S.P. is M.E. +3D6 at level one, plus 1D6+1 per additional level of experience. Clairvoyance (4), Mind Block (4), and Telepathy (4), plus five powers of choice from the Sensitive category. All knockers are Major Psychics.

Knocking (special): This is a limited form of Telekinesis that produces a sound similar to a hammer tap. Knockers use this ability to signal places of danger, usually places where a cave-in is imminent. Range: line of sight. Duration: One hour per level of experience. I.S.P.: 6.

Enemies: Kobolds, Goblins, Hob-Goblins, Orcs, Ogres, Trolls, and most of the so-called monster races.

Allies: Humans, Elves, and Faerie Folk, but are shy and reclusive, preferring to aid through indirect means.

Attacks per Melee: Standard.

Bonuses: +1 to save vs poison and disease, +1 to save vs mind control and possession.

Habitat: Can be found almost anywhere that mines and natural cave systems exist.

Favorite Weapons: Any weapon small enough to be used.

Other Notes: Like Gnomes, Knockers have difficulty finding clothing, armor, weapons, and tools that are small enough for them (when outside their own kingdoms). They can use Gnome-sized weapons normally (half the damage of human-sized weapons), or can use human-sized weapons with penalties of -6 to strike and parry, and -6 to dodge if the weapon is heavier than a knife or dagger.

Lutin

Lutins (the u is pronounced like the German ü) are believed by some to be the "missing link" between Faeries and Goblins. They are physically similar to Hob-Goblins, albeit far more attractive, but have a temperament and powers more like Faeries. Lutins also lack the underground abilities of most sub-human races.

Lutins live in underground settlements consisting of roughly made tunnels and chambers. They are friendly folk, so their social hierarchy and foreign relations are completely different from other sub-human races. They are not tribal so much as civic, practicing direct democracy with universal adult suffrage. Most settlements use a system similar to post-Enlightenment Western nations: the three-branch Executive, Legislative, Judicial system, with the general populace taking the role and duties of a Legislature and directly electing not just the Mayor but the heads of all departments (Police Chief, Fire Chief, Hospital Administrator, etc.) and Judges.

Visitors are always welcome, and Lutins are quick to offer hospitality and trade. Most settlements offer naturalization, allowing foreigners, even non-Lutins, the ability to become full-voting citizens. They do display some of the Faerie tendency towards mischievousness, but understand the limits of physical bodies and are careful not to take things too far.

Lutins are about the same size as Hob-Goblins, and have similar ears, but are considerably prettier. They do not make Faerie Rings, Food, Drink, or weapons, and do not glow, but do have the Faeries' instinctive spell-casting abilities.

Alignment: Any, but lean towards Unprincipled and Anarchist.

Attributes: I.Q. 2D6+6, M.E. 3D6+6, M.A. 3D6, P.S. 3D6, P.P. 3D6, P.E. 3D6, P.B. 3D6, Spd 3D6 running, 1D6 digging.

Hit Points: P.E. +1D6 per level of experience.

S.D.C.: Standard.

P.P.E.: 1D6x100

Horror Factor: None.

Physical Appearance: Short compared to humans, with large ears and bald head.

Size: 4-5 feet (1.2-1.5 m).

Weight: 90-140 pounds (41-63 kg).

Average Life Span: 80+ years.

Natural Abilities: Nightvision 40 feet (12.2 m), excellent day vision, keen hearing (see bonuses).

Magic: Charm, Mend Wood, Metamorphosis: Animal (the Invocation, not the Cobbler Goblin ability), See the Invisible, Sense Magic, Tongues, and Wither Plants. The normal Faerie Magic rules apply: Victims need to roll a 16 or higher to save; spell effectiveness, duration, and range are equal to a tenth level spell caster; spells do not consume the Lutin's own P.P.E.; spells can be cast on other individuals as often as once per 24 hours; no additional spells can be learned (all Magic O.C.C.s are unavailable); impervious to magic cast by other Lutins.

Psionics: None.

Enemies: Banshees, most demons, the undead, and obviously mean supernatural beings, forces of evil, and intolerant, cranky fuddy-duddies with no sense of humor. They dislike Goblins, Hob-Goblins, Kobolds, and Orcs.

Allies: Faerie Folk are not allies per se, but these distant relatives will be friendly towards Lutins, will not pull pranks on them, and may come to their aid and vice versa, especially if the individual is known.

Attacks per Melee: As per O.C.C. and skills. Up to two magic spells can be cast per melee, each in place of half the normal melee actions/attacks.

Bonuses: +1 to save vs magic, +1 to save vs possession.

Habitat: Can be found almost anywhere on Rifts Earth. They are known to build "undercities" that coexist with surface settlements in locations that lack subterranean infrastructure such as sewer or underground water pipes.

Favorite Weapons: Will use any weapons.

Pech

These strange, diminutive humanoids are sometimes confused with Gnomes and Spriggans. They are broadly similar in appearance and habits to Gnomes, with the addition of Supernatural Strength. They build spectacular stone works, like Spriggans, except that their focus is not on megalithic structures, but on sturdy, well-designed buildings covered completely in beautiful sculpture.

Pechs are highly secretive, and seek out wilderness areas far from existing cities. Although not unfriendly, they will be aloof with visitors, keeping their heads down and keeping conversations short when confronted. They have a great love for beautiful things, so artists, especially sculptors, can win them over.

Alignment: Any.

Attributes: I.Q. 3D6, M.E. 3D6, M.A. 2D6, P.S. 3D6+12, P.P. 4D6, P.E. 4D6, P.B. 2D6, Spd 2D6.

Hit Points: P.E. +1D6 per level of experience.

S.D.C.: Standard.

P.P.E.: 1D4x10

R.C.C. Skills: All Pechs have the following skills in addition to O.C.C. Skills: Carpentry +5%, General Repair, Masonry +10%, Sculpting and Whittling +10%.

Horror Factor: None.

Physical Appearance: Small, burly humanoids, typically with red or brown hair.

Size: 3-4 feet (0.9-1.2 m).

Weight: 50-90 pounds (23-41 kg).

Average Life Span: 600 years.

Natural Abilities: Supernatural Strength.

Magic: As per O.C.C.

Psionics: Roll 1D100: 01-20 Major Psionics, 21-50 Minor Psionics, 51-00 No Psionics.

Enemies: None per se, but hate trespassers violently.

Allies: None.

Attacks per Melee: As per O.C.C. and skills.

Bonuses: As per Supernatural Strength.

Habitat: Can live in any environment a human can, but prefer secluded places with a ready stone supply where they can live in peace.

Favorite Weapons: Prefer mattock and hammer-style weapons.

Other Notes: None.

Dawn of a New Era

An Adventure for Heroes Unlimited™

By Corey Livermore

Introduction

The year is 2036, and it is the dawn of a new age of mankind. Although there has been rampant speculation for as long as anyone can remember about the existence of aliens and super-powered humans, it has only been within the last 5 years that these beings have made themselves known. Nobody is quite sure anymore which happened first – either aliens landed on Earth bringing about the need for super-powered humans, or super-powered humans emerged on Earth bringing about the need for aliens to protect us from ourselves. The one thing that is certain is that they are both here, and they both appear to be here for good.

Fear is what drives mortals to do some of the worst things. Some of the most despicable acts ever carried out have arisen from fear of the unknown or misunderstood. And the evolution of our own species, combined with the discovery that we are not alone in the universe, has caused a widespread panic amongst all of mankind across the entire globe. This panic has, inevitably, led to all super-powered beings and aliens being classified as dangerous and evil.

62 countries around the world have created, passed, and implemented some form of anti-superbeing legislation. In the worst pieces of legislation, such as those in Sudan, Chad, Yemen, and Iran, being accused and convicted of being a super-powered human or alien brings the death penalty. In other countries such as Japan, Canada, and England, super-powered beings must be registered as such, along with their abilities, contacts, personal background, and any other information as required by the government. In some militaristic countries, such as China, North Korea, and Russia, super-powered beings are encouraged to come forth so that they may be studied and their abilities replicated for the military.

America has always been known for tolerance and understanding, but the new threat of super-powered beings and aliens has caused mass hysteria in all levels of government. The fear of not being able to protect our own borders has caused 27 states to pass some form of anti-superbeing legislation. And there is a growing concern among the people that state law may not be enough. While the states have the power to create and pass any legislation they choose, none of the state laws makes it a crime to

be a super-powered being or alien so long as the person or alien comes forward and registers as such. Failure to register is a crime, and does carry a jail sentence.

The problem with registration in America, and elsewhere in the world, is that the superbeings are out in public, with their true identities always known by all. And with so many people afraid of being on the wrong end of a super-powered being, some areas of the country have been hit by riots and lynch mobs, ready to take care of the "superbeing problem." So most super-powered beings do not make themselves known. Fear, again, has caused the evolution of mankind to take a temporary back seat.

To quell the public's fears about super-powered beings, and to make registration mandatory no matter what state you live in, legislation was introduced into the House of Representatives by Secoro Gonzalez, a Republican from New Mexico. The bill has gained serious traction, and a vote on it is expected any day now. If it should pass the House, it will go on to the Senate, where it is expected to sit until after the coming presidential election. And then the fate of the bill will rest in the hands of whomever wins.

The Democratic candidate, the incumbent President Alice Darford, is against the anti-superbeing legislation. She feels that forcing superbeings and aliens to register is akin to being in Germany during World War II. She fears that forcing them to register will only encourage lynch mobs and rioters to seek out the superbeings and cause them harm. She refuses to put anybody in harm's way unless absolutely necessary, and therefore would veto the legislation should it pass and get to her desk.

The Republican candidate, New Mexico Governor Prio Gonzalez, is for the anti-superhero legislation. Like his twin brother Secoro, Prio feels that super-powered beings and aliens should make themselves known to all. He is quoted on multiple occasions as saying that to allow them to move secretly among us is to threaten our own borders and homeland security from within. Should the legislation pass and make it to his desk, he would sign it into law almost immediately.

In the polls currently, Prio is killing Alice. The general public feels that superbeings should be registered, and that they are a threat to the American way of life. The public stands behind any man or woman who is willing to stand up for their rights, even if it means taking away the rights of some citizens. And that's exactly how the superhero community feels – their rights are being taken away.

So this is where you are. In a country that wants to make you an outsider when all you want to do is help. Thankfully, you are in Chicago, where there is no anti-superbeing legislation. You are free to be yourself – your true self – should you choose to do

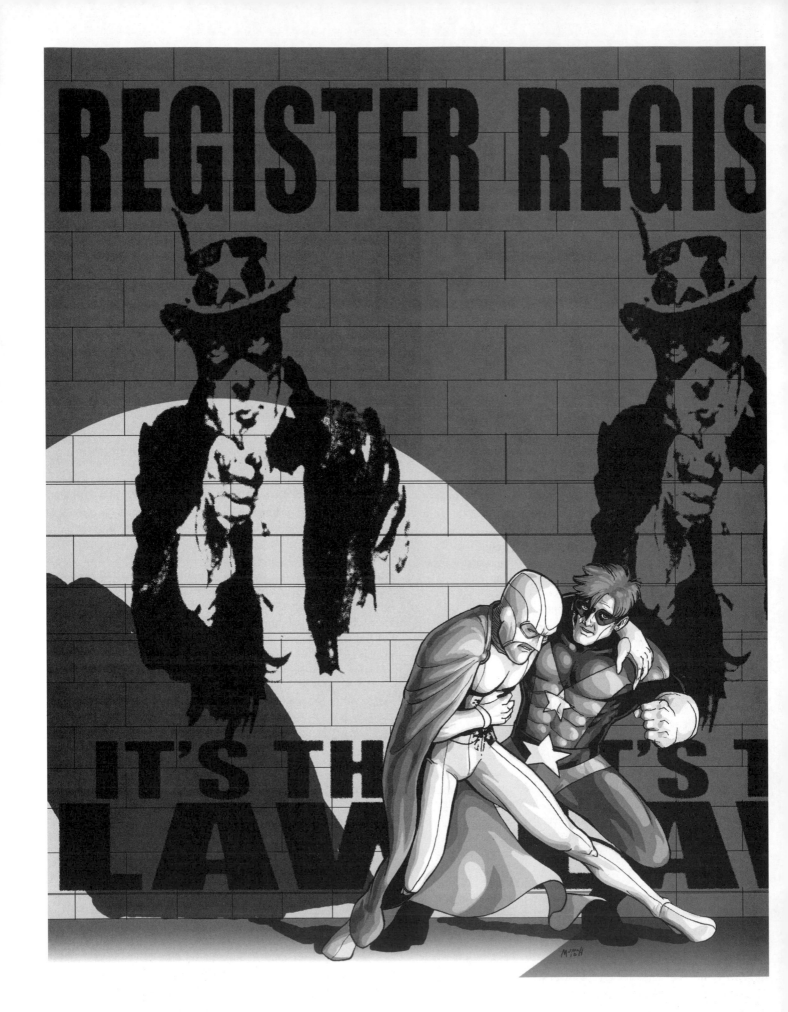

that. All you really have to do is wait until the opportunity to be yourself presents itself...

What this Is

Dawn of a New Era is a multi-faceted, massive campaign for the **Heroes Unlimited™ Role-Playing Game** designed and sold by Palladium Books®. The campaign is designed for 4-6 player characters, starting at 1st level, and is to be played from start to finish, although any individual chapter or section of this adventure may be taken and played independently of the other portions. It is up to the Game Master to decide which pieces of this adventure are to be played, and which ones are not (should any portions not be played). However, the campaign is best played in its entirety, as the events in one section do play into the events in the next and subsequent sections.

What You Need in Addition to This

So, you can't just use this by itself? Unfortunately, no. Well, not unless you have the entire set of rules memorized and can spit them out on command. This is not designed to be used on its own, but rather to be used as an adventure or campaign for characters that are created using the core rules.

So what do you need in addition to this adventure? You will need (or should have easy access to):
● *Heroes Unlimited™, 2nd Edition*
● *Powers Unlimited™ 1*
● *Powers Unlimited™ 2*
● *Powers Unlimited™ 3*
● Paper, pencils, and dice.
● A vivid imagination.
● A strong desire to play *Heroes Unlimited™*.

We understand that not everyone may have access to *Powers Unlimited™ 1, 2* and *3*, and that's ok. You can still use this book with just the core rules found in *Heroes Unlimited™, 2nd Edition*, with only some minor irritations. There are some characters and powers in this campaign that come from the *Powers Unlimited™* supplements, so it is recommended that you have them. But if you don't have those books, feel free to substitute any powers or power categories that you don't have information on with those that you do. Or you can substitute entire non-player characters or enemies if you wish.

If you are someone who is going to be participating in this campaign as a player character, you should stop reading. The information contained in the rest of this adventure is for the G.M.'s eyes only. If you are going to have a player character in a campaign that involves any portion of the information contained in this adventure, reading about it before playing through it will only spoil the fun you will be having. It is therefore recommended that you do not continue reading unless you are going to be the G.M. of this campaign.

G.M. Information

From this point on, everything will be detailed as though you are the G.M. Information about enemies, locations, powers, spells, etc., follows. Before we can get into those details, there are a few tips that you may need while reading this adventure.

1. Where applicable, sentences and/or paragraphs that can be read directly to the players have a border or box around them. You may read these word-for-word, or you can paraphrase them as you see fit. These are included to help you give the right atmosphere for the events that are taking place.

2. None of the NPCs that are contained in this book have any skill check percentages listed. This is done not to conserve space, but to allow you to have a little bit of freedom in determining if a particular NPC actually succeeds in a skill check. Furthermore, most of the NPCs detailed herein (if not all of them) are enemies that the characters will face, and in most situations a skill check is not going to be required.

3. Some of the skill programs that are listed were obtained from the topic *Education Table and Skill Programs, Redux*, which can be found at the Palladium Megaverse® forums (the site address for this topic is http://forums.palladium-megaverse. com/viewtopic.php?t=78912).

4. Only the stats for an NPC that are relevant or have a value are listed. If an NPC doesn't have a bonus to save vs magic, that stat won't be listed. This was done to conserve as much space as possible, while making it easy to show you what the NPC can do.

5. The events in the campaign take place in multiple locations throughout the United States, most notably Chicago, Illinois and Albuquerque, New Mexico, although the players will find themselves in the Nevada desert at one point. Although maps have been provided of the major areas in these cities, it is recommended that you familiarize yourself with these cities so that there is less confusion about where things are taking place. Of course, you can always just exchange the locations for places that you are familiar with!

Part I: The Start of an Ugly Friendship

The campaign starts in Chicago, IL, in the middle of spring. You can read the below to the players or you can paraphrase as you see fit:

> *Ah, Chicago in April. Springtime is definitely in the air, and people all around the city are excited for the things the year can bring. There are always so many things to participate in and watch that it's amazing people have time to fit them all in.*
>
> *Springtime means baseball, and Cubs fans are hoping that this year is the year the curse is finally broken. 128 years have passed since the Cubs won the World Series,*

and with every passing year the fans get more and more disillusioned about their chances. The White Sox, on the other hand, are the defending World Series champions, and their fans know that this year they have a great chance to repeat.

Basketball is also in full swing, with the Bulls standing at 4 games over .500 and needing to win all of their remaining games and get some help in order to get into the playoffs. It doesn't look good, though, as the Milwaukee Bucks have a 2 game lead and an easy schedule down the stretch. If only the Bulls had beaten the Cavaliers and Rockets in their last 2 games...

Hockey is going strong, and the Blackhawks look poised to go for the 3-peat as Stanley Cup champions. The 'Hawks secured their spot in the playoffs almost 3 weeks ago, and have cruised into being the President's Cup winner with well over 100 points. The team is strong, and their fans are rabid with anticipation.

The only sport not in full swing is football, but the draft is coming and everybody loves the draft. Too bad the Bears are one of the worst teams in the league, having not won more than 6 games in a single season since 2014. 21 years of absolute futility is starting to wear on the fans, and even the league has stepped in to try to reverse the team's fortunes. It also doesn't help that a beloved former coach and Chicago legend recently passed away at the age of 95.

There is still snow on the ground in places, and the wind running through the city off of Lake Michigan will chill people to the bone, but there isn't anywhere any of the residents would rather be. Chicago is a unique town, with unique opportunities. Republican presidential hopeful Prio Gonzalez will be in town in the coming weeks for a series of speeches on homeland security and national defense, while the incumbent, President Alice Darford, hopes to come into the city to give her views of the major issues.

The above sets the tone for this portion of the campaign. Chicago, IL, in Spring is a great place to be, but it can get cold and things can get ugly quick. Players should already be thinking about deep dish pizza and chili dogs. But before they can get too far into their thoughts, an attack at the Daley Center (the Cook County Courthouse) will bring them back to reality.

For those characters who are near or watching a television, the following should be read:

> There normally isn't much on television on a Wednesday at noon. Soap operas and the occasional re-run of Jerry Springer just don't seem to have any flair or style. Thankfully, you only had to endure 5 or so minutes of this before the news cut in with a live report.
>
> "This is Joanne Gorven with WMAQ-TV, NBC Channel 5, and we're receiving reports that there has been an explosion on Washington Street right outside the Daley Center. Calls have been coming in from multiple witnesses saying that... wait, is the teleprompter right? Someone is flying over the street, shooting up the area?
>
> "Anyhow, witnesses tell us that at least 3 or 4 police cars have been totally destroyed, and all civilians have been evacuated from the immediate area. We're being told that the police have set up blockades on both Dearborn and

> Clark in an attempt to prevent people from driving through the area.
>
> "We have a camera crew en route, and once we are able to get a live feed from the area, we will break in again to keep you updated on this story..."

For those characters who are near or listening to the radio, the following should be read:

> Why is it the good music is always the stuff that gets pre-empted? Just when your favorite song was starting, the idiot DJ had to break in and get all fired up about something.
>
> "Sorry to break into the song, folks, but we're getting reports from our listeners here at WDRV that there's been an explosion at the Daley Center. Eyewitness reports are a little sketchy yet, but it seems as though someone is flying around shooting up the place. We're not sure if they mean that someone is running around the area with a gun or if they are actually flying, but we'll try to get as much information as we can and get a better report for you.
>
> "In the meantime, we'll take you back to the song you were listening to..."

If the player characters are not near a television or a radio, one of the following should be told to the players:

- Someone they know rushes in to wherever they are at and begins telling them very loudly that there has been an explosion at the Daley Center, and that there is a live news crew on the TV right now explaining all about it; OR
- They are in the vicinity of the Daley Center when the explosion takes place.

Players should not be *inside* the Daley Center unless their specific character background indicates that they would be.

No matter which scenario above plays out, the players at this point will know that something is happening at the Daley Center. They should also suspect that a super-powered person is the one causing the commotion, based on the reports about someone flying around. Most players will know that this is the start of the campaign and this is an adventure hook, and will want to go straight to the courthouse without asking any other questions. Let them do this – they are heroes, after all, and what hero doesn't want to investigate an explosion in the middle of a city?

Once on the scene, the players' suspicions will be confirmed. A super-powered individual is flying above the street. This person does not have any visible means of flying, and he is covered head-to-toe with some form of metallic armor. The metallic-clad assailant is Gregory Solcka, a 1st level Super Invention character.

Gregory Solcka

1st Level Super Invention (Hardware, Mechanical Genius)
Attributes: I.Q. 15, M.E. 12, M.A. 14, P.S. 15, P.P. 14, P.E. 7, P.B. 14, Spd 4.
Hit Points: 13, **S.D.C.:** 32, **A.R.:** 4.
Combat: Attacks per Melee: 4
Pull Punch: +2
Roll: +2
The Sponsoring Organization: Independent. Gregory is the inventor.
Who is the Character: The chosen operator or test pilot.
Motive to Create the Device: Revenge.

Physical Appearance of the Gizmo: Cape/Cloak. A.R. 7, 200 S.D.C.

Power Level of the Super Abilities: Equal to 3rd level in power-er.

Major:

Bio-Armor

- Only the full armor version.
- A.R. 16
- 260 S.D.C.
- +1 P.S.
- +1D6 to melee attacks.

Minor:

Flight, Wingless

- +1 attack.
- +2 to strike.
- +2 to parry.
- +4 to dodge at slower than 80 mph (128 km).
- +6 to dodge faster than 80 mph (128 km).

Energy Shield

- +3 to parry.

Energy Expulsion: Energy

- 4D6 damage.
- +3 to strike aimed, +1 to strike when not aimed.

Education Level: High School Graduate.

Skill Program 1: Mechanical Genius

- Aircraft Mechanics
- Automotive Mechanics
- Basic Electronics
- Basic Mechanics
- Build Super Vehicle
- Hot Wire Automobile
- Locksmith
- Mathematics: Advanced
- Mechanical Engineer
- Pilot: Motorcycle
- Pilot: Race Car
- Read Sensory Equipment
- Recognize Vehicle Quality
- Robot Mechanics
- Weapons Engineer

Skill Program 2: Gizmoteer, Robot Construction

- Armorer
- Artificial Intelligence
- Circuit Board Micro-Electronics
- Electronic Counter-Measures
- Computer Operation
- Computer Programming
- Computer Repair
- Electrical Engineer
- Robot Electronics

8 Secondary Skills

- Astronomy
- Hand to Hand: Basic
- Literacy
- Pilot Automobile
- Radio: Basic
- Research
- T.V. & Video
- Writing

Gregory is flying around shooting bolts of energy because he is attempting to kill Louis Jackson, who is being led into the courthouse by 2 armed police officers. Louis is handcuffed, with his arms behind his back, and he has been arrested for selling drugs. Gregory wants to kill him because he sold the drugs to his sister that killed her. He is after revenge, and he won't stop until he gets it.

There are 3 different scenarios that will happen here. The first is that Gregory isn't killed but is stopped and incapacitated in some way, allowing the police to take him into custody. This won't be easy, but will earn the characters the trust and respect of the Chicago Police Department. This is the best track for the players to take as they will be able to be contacted openly by the police department about helping them bring other criminals and supers to justice. Once detained, both Gregory and his cloak are taken into custody. The players may try all they want, but the cloak is evidence and is not going with the players under this scenario.

If Gregory is killed during the fight, the characters will be blamed for his death and this will not only gain them notoriety but will immediately put them on Chicago's Most Wanted list. The characters may end up with his cloak in the event he is killed, but if they do only a Hardware character will be able to figure out how it works. In fact, the cloak is tailored specifically for Gregory, and it responds only to his DNA. A Hardware character (specifically an Analytical Genius) or a Natural Genius may (01-10% chance) be able to figure out how to alter the cloak to be usable by another person, but there will always be a small (01-10%) chance that the cloak will not function properly all the time.

The final scenario that may play out is that Louis is killed and Gregory begins his escape. This is the least likely scenario, but must be detailed here in the event it happens. Gregory's flight speed is 260 mph (416 km) maximum, and this may make it hard for the players to keep up with him. If none of the characters has flight or a way to keep up with him, he unfortunately escapes. This in turn earns the characters the ire of the Chicago Police Department for interfering. In this event, Gregory is available to turn up later in the campaign at your discretion to deal with the people who tried to stop him. You may also have the characters do some research to find Gregory and confront him on their terms.

If there is a character who can keep up with Gregory, or even slow him down enough, the fight can continue. Although Louis is dead, Gregory still needs to be brought to justice. At this point, one of the first two scenarios will happen in that Gregory will either be killed or brought to justice. The information about his cloak remains unchanged.

The stats to be used for Louis Jackson:

- A.R. 4
- 20 S.D.C.
- 10 Hit Points.

Louis will not have any attacks as he is handcuffed, and he doesn't receive any bonuses to dodge any attacks because of this.

All officers on the scene, including the ones at both blockades (except for Lt. Steven Draskal), have the following stats:

- An A.R. of 10 due to wearing a concealed vest (75 S.D.C.).
- A 9mm (3D6) or a 5.56mm rifle (5D6).
- A fiberglass nightstick (1D4) or a steel rod encased nightstick (1D6).

- 4 attacks per combat round.
- +2 to strike, dodge, parry, and initiative.
- 20 S.D.C.
- 20 Hit Points.

Lt. Steven Draskal will be at the northern barricade, and at this time his presence is only as the commander of the operation to stop Gregory. The stats for Lt. Draskal are given later in this section, as he will play a minor role in the story. He is wearing a Point Blank Vest (A.R. 10, 70 S.D.C.) and is carrying a .44 Magnum (6D6 damage). During the fight that ensues, Lt. Draskal will probably be encountered by at least 1 of the players as they are trying to make their way through the northern barricade to help. He will order the player(s) who attempt this to stop, but he will not have them shot at or arrested for interfering with a police operation.

Police officers will definitely shoot at Gregory, but they will probably not shoot at the characters. There is a chance (01-10%) that the officers will continue to shoot at Gregory even if he is engaged in melee combat with one of the characters. In this event, any roll to strike that is under a 10 (Gregory's A.R. is 16 due to Bio-Armor) may strike the player that is in melee combat with Gregory. You will need to roll a normal strike roll to see if the player is hit.

Gregory is the first test the players will face. He has his Bio-Armor up and activated, and is ready to dish out some pain. His motive is right, but his methods are not. He is considered to be a super-villain, and taking him out will earn the characters some brownie points with the media and the police.

It may seem that Gregory is an easy target, but the opposite is true. 260 S.D.C. is a lot for a group of 4-6 player characters to deal with, especially if they don't have any true offensive powers. It may take the players a good amount of time to deal with him, and this is true seeing as they don't know each other yet and haven't had time to play around with combat strategy or coordinate attacks with other players.

After the fight is over, Lt. Draskal will approach the players and offer his thanks, as well as the general thanks of the Chicago Police Department. He will ask simple questions of the players, such as who they are, how they got there so fast, etc. He won't be overtly trying to pump them for information, but will use his detective skills to get as much info as possible. Any information that he gets from the characters he will pass on to his contacts at ConGenix, which will in turn be forwarded to either Prio Gonzalez. Either way, Prio gets the information about the characters, which can then be used by him.

Later that same evening or the following day, whichever works better for the campaign, the events outside the courthouse have been picked up by the national news wire. There are multiple news reports on TV, on the radio, and in the newspapers regarding what happened. While the characters are not named outright, their descriptions are given in fantastic detail, along with what they did during the fight. The only way the characters can stay out of the news is if they were not witnessed participating in any capacity (which is next to impossible). It is possible that the characters may have given their names to local police or the news stations, and as such, the news stories may give their names.

The news stories also contain quotes from Secoro Gonzalez, a Republican from New Mexico in the House of Representatives.

Read the following to the players regarding what Secoro has said about the incident:

> *"The bill that I have introduced will make it mandatory for all super-powered individuals and aliens to register as such. The mandatory information they must supply includes, but is not limited to: their name, any aliases they may have, any super powers they may have, and their full criminal records.*
>
> *"There is one provision of this bill that I am sincerely hoping is not line-item vetoed, and that is the provision on DNA. The bill, in its current form, states that, when registering, a super-powered being MUST provide a sample of their DNA to be kept on record. I know that my opponents to this bill feel that this is nothing more than an attempt to make these super-powered beings similar to criminals. I say that they may be right. But I ask this: Would you want one of these people hurting the ones you love, with powers that you and the police of this great nation are unable to counter?*
>
> *"The incident at the Daley Center in Chicago is the exact reason why we need to have this legislation passed. If super-powered individuals are allowed to roam the city streets unchecked, we will end up with the same disaster in all of our cities across this great nation. We must act, and we must act now."*

Secoro Gonzalez is portrayed as the twin brother of Prio Gonzalez, the Republican presidential hopeful from the state of New Mexico. Secoro is, in fact, a Multiple Self of Prio, not merely his twin. The players should not, under any circumstances, find out this information at any time prior to their incarceration at the Moon Prison (see the end of *Part II: Which Way Did They Go, George* and the beginning of *Part III: Home Sweet Home Away From Home* for more details). All the players need to know at this point is that both Prio and Secoro (although they are the same person) are attempting to have new laws passed restricting the possession and use of super powers.

A few days after the incidents at the Daley Center, one of the characters will be contacted by the Chicago Police Department (if Gregory is not killed), or by a seedy underworld contact (if Gregory is killed). The character contacted should have traits that are likable by the person contacting them - a high P.B., serious sense of loyalty and honor, possible police skill program if contacted by the police; selfish alignment, criminal record prior to becoming a hero, nefarious other contacts if contacted by the underworld.

No matter which character is contacted, and no matter who contacts the character, the reason for the contact is the same: a known drug lord by the name of Percy "Hard-Nose" Harrison, who has not won any favors with anybody thanks to his policy of shoot first-shoot second-forget the questions, is expecting a shipment of guns and drugs sometime in the near future, and there are certain people in high positions within the city that do not want this shipment to reach him. Because the characters have been seen in the news as heroes (or, if they allowed Gregory to be killed, as vigilantes), they are being contacted with an offer to help make it so this shipment doesn't arrive.

If the players are contacted by the police, they are being asked to do their city and country a favor by helping to take down this criminal. If the players are being contacted by a criminal figure,

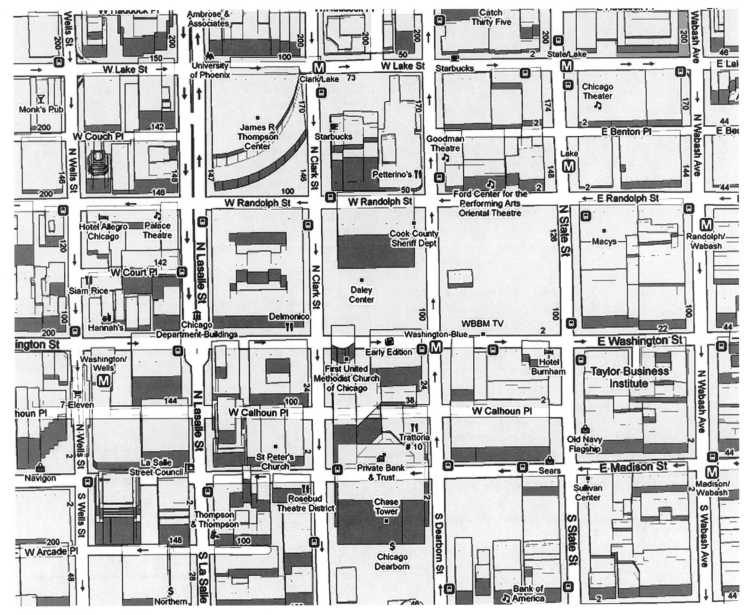

they are being coerced to take Harrison out under threat of their location being given to the local police (remember, if they are being contacted by a criminal then it's due to them having killed Gregory Solcka and they are now wanted by the police as criminals themselves). Either way, the only information that they can be given about the shipment at this time is that it is coming in the near future (1-2 weeks, exact day and time not known), and that it is coming in through the Chicago harbor area. That is all the contact knows, and it is up to the players from this point on to figure out where, when, and how to stop it.

At this point, the players will need to do some research and investigation into Percy Harrison and his illegal doings. On a successful research check, consult the following table and either roll randomly for a piece of information, or pick one and give it to the players:

1. Percy has previously spent time in the Pontiac Correctional Facility for assault (2 years).

2. Percy had a cellmate at the Pontiac Correctional Facility named "Low-Life" Jones who is now living in Chicago.

3. It is rumored that Percy always has at least 6 guards around him at any time.

4. Percy only leaves his house on Saturday mornings to go out for breakfast.

5. Percy is skilled with a handgun.

6. Several police officers are rumored to be on Percy's payroll, including a Lieutenant Draskal.

7. It is rumored that Percy has connections to government officials outside the state of Illinois.

8. Percy is keeping up appearances of being a law-abiding citizen by donating money to churches and other charitable entities.

All of the above statements are true except for #4 (Percy likes to go out for breakfast, but this isn't the only activity that he leaves his house for) and #6 (Lt. Draskal is friendly/sympathetic to Percy, but is not on his payroll).

The players will also need to ask some questions in the seedier parts of town to determine when and where exactly the drugs and guns are coming in. Again, on a successful research check, consult the following table and either roll randomly for a piece of information, or pick one and give it to the players:

1. The shipment contains 1,000 kilos of cocaine.

2. The shipment contains 500 assault rifles and ammunition.

3. The shipment is coming in on a Saturday.

4. The shipment is coming in on a Sunday.
5. The shipment is coming in at night.
6. The shipment is coming in during the early morning.
7. The shipment is coming in through Navy Pier.
8. The shipment is coming in through Chicago Harbor.
9. The shipment is coming in on a large boat.
10. The shipment is coming in on several smaller boats.

As you can see, there are many conflicting statements. Dealing with people of less than noble character will generally yield untrue statements about what is going to be happening. The statements above that are true are #1, #2, #4, #5, #8 and #10. The shipment contains a lot of cocaine, a lot of guns, and is going to be on a Sunday night at Chicago Harbor, and is being brought by several smaller boats.

Players at this point should be relatively confused as to when and where the shipment is coming in. It's ok if this happens – they are dealing with criminals who may not be honest with them. The only way that they will be able to find out the exact place and time, with truth, is to track down Percy Harrison and question him about it. Which shouldn't be all too hard – his current address is on file with the police department. If any characters talk to the police department and ask for Percy's address, that character receives a bonus 100 Experience Points for eliminating all of the other ground work.

At any rate, the players should want to go and track down Percy and talk to him. Percy will have been forewarned about the players, as they should have gotten his address from the police station. This will cause Lt. Draskal to call Percy and give him a heads-up. When the players arrive at Percy's house, they will be invited in only to be ambushed immediately by Percy and his 6 bodyguards.

Each of the 6 bodyguards will have the following statistics:
- An A.R. of 8 due to wearing some type of leather or padded jacket (with 50 S.D.C.).
- Either a .22 (2D4), a 9mm (3D6) or a .44 (6D6) for a weapon.
- 4 attacks per combat round.

- +2 to strike.
- +1 to dodge.
- 30 S.D.C.
- 20 Hit Points.

The bodyguards are pretty nondescript. Average height and weight, all dressed in jeans and leather jackets. They all have at least 1 clothing item on them that is yellow, most likely a t-shirt underneath the leather jacket or their shoes. This color is the color of the gang that Percy runs, and all members are required to wear it.

Percy Harrison has the following statistics:
- An A.R. of 10 due to wearing a concealed vest (75 S.D.C.).
- A 5.56mm rifle (5D6).
- 4 attacks per combat round.
- +2 to strike, dodge, parry and initiative.
- 50 S.D.C.
- 40 Hit Points.

Percy Harrison is a short, fat, black man with a greasy afro and a matching soul patch. He wears thick glasses, and has earrings in both ears. He will be wearing a yellow suit, which makes him look something like an overweight canary, but he thinks he is totally pimped out. His concealed vest is worn underneath the jacket of the suit.

At first, the characters will be held at gunpoint and questioned about why they are there. If any character mentions the shipment, the bodyguards will open fire. If the characters state that they only wish to talk, Percy will question them why, having his guards put their weapons down. He will not accept any answer they give him, growing angrier and angrier by the minute. He has become paranoid thanks to years of drug use. This situation will eventually evolve into combat, and the players should realize they are outnumbered.

There are 2 possible outcomes here: Percy and all of his men are killed, or Percy is captured alive. If Percy is killed, the characters will need to search him and his house to find the details of

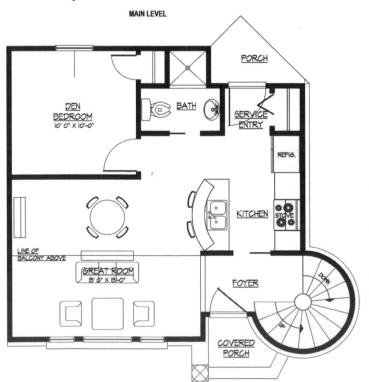

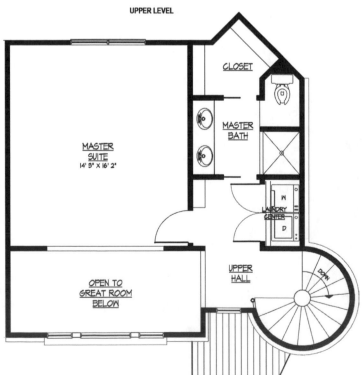

the shipment. On his person, Percy has a key in the shape of a small yacht on a chain in one of his pockets. The key is to a safe that is in his bedroom on the second floor of his house, which is covered by a picture of the yacht that is the basis of the key. The safe contains several documents that have information about the shipment, including where and when. There is also a document in his safe that is stamped with the corporate logo of ConGenix.

ConGenix, should the players inquire, is a technology and research firm with their headquarters in Albuquerque, New Mexico. They are the leading company as far as genetic engineering, space transportation, and they provide military and security services to multiple companies and countries throughout the world. If the players ask for more information than this, all they should be told is that the document in Percy's safe appears to be an invoice for some experimental medical product, but the details of that product are sketchy at best. It should be noted that ConGenix plays a major role in this campaign, and the players will eventually be led there.

If Percy is captured alive, the players will still be able to find the information about the shipment and obtain the document from ConGenix, but there are major bonuses to be had by capturing him:

1. They will be able to turn him in to the police. With the evidence of the drug shipment, as well as his goons opening fire on the players, this wins big style points with the police and the media.

2. They will be able to question him about ConGenix, and what the medication is. He can only say that the medication is supposed to help treat his diabetes, but with a successful interrogation or intimidation check, he will reveal that he hasn't felt quite right the last couple of days. If pressed, all he'll say is that he feels like he's someone else, but living in his skin. The medication is, in fact, in the beginning stages of giving him the minor ability of Alter Physical Body.

3. Percy will talk about a number of topics, mostly things he is interested in (like sex) or girls he's nailed. Attentive characters may hear him mention a "grey-mustached pig screwing me over all the time," which is Percy's way of selling out Lt. Draskal.

If the characters end up capturing him, they will receive a bonus of 150 Experience Points each on top of the Experience Point award for subduing a criminal/foe.

No matter which scenario plays out above, they will be in for a rude awakening if and/or once they reach the docks – the shipment will not arrive. If Percy is killed, the police find out about his demise and Lt. Draskal will cancel the shipment due to being paranoid about the players intercepting it. If the players bring Percy to the police station, Lt. Draskal will again cancel the shipment due to paranoia. The shipment is never going to be available for the players to intercept, so it is in their best interests to capture Percy to gain the extra Experience Points.

At this point, the characters should be at least 2nd level. If they are not, it is recommended that a few side adventures take place so that they can get up to 2nd level, if not to 3rd.

The aftermath of arresting or killing Percy will not be good for the characters. While they are going to be regarded as heroes in the local media, Secoro Gonzalez will be all over the media calling for the characters to be branded as vigilantes (especially if Percy is killed), and that they are nothing more than a menace to society. A few days after the incident with Percy, the following news story comes out (which can be read to the players):

> *Another day, another incident in Chicago. And it seems that the local "super-heroes" in the windy city are becoming more of a problem than they are a solution.*
>
> *In a recent incident, presumed drug lord Percy "Hard-Nose" Harrison was killed by the super-powered sleuths, in what can only be described as a gruesome fashion. There wasn't much left of his body to identify when it was found, with only dental records to prove who it was.*
>
> *The charred remains of his body were found this morning on the dock near his boat in Chicago Harbor. Police are unsure as to how his body was burned that badly, as no accelerant was found on or near him, but Lt. Steven Draskal of the Chicago police had this to say:*
>
> *"While we don't know how his body was burned in this fashion, we do know that the so-called 'supers' who assisted with the incident at the Daley Center do have abilities that would allow them to do this to another human being. Why they would want to do this is another story. I guess it's just in their nature to abuse whatever power they think they have."*
>
> *New Mexico Representative Secoro Gonzalez had these comments when questioned about the rise of super-powered individuals:*
>
> *"These people need to be stopped. The individuals in Chicago are a prime example of what can happen when people end up with power that they don't understand or control. They are nothing more than a menace to society, and their criminal actions have shown us that they have no regard for human life or the laws of society. I am asking all law enforcement officials to take heed of the warning they have already given us, and I ask that these people turn themselves in to the proper authorities."*
>
> *As of today, no arrests have been made, and the individuals are still not in custody. Police have stated that these super-heroes are to be considered armed and extremely dangerous, and they should not approached by anyone.*

The above news story should completely shock the players, especially if they didn't end up killing Percy. The characters should get the idea from this story that they are being made to be an example of why the super-hero registration bill needs to be made into law. The biggest thing in the above story that should alert the characters is the words of Lt. Draskal. They may have gone to him regarding Percy, and his words should ring out that he is not what he makes himself appear to be.

The next time that all of the players are together in a building of some sort, which may be immediately after they hear/read the news story, a team of 6 highly trained and armed officers/military personnel will storm the room and attempt to kill them. The characters are in danger, and they should fight back. Each of the officers has the following stats:

- Full suit of Riot Armor (A.R. 14, 180 S.D.C.).
- A .45 M3 (4D6).
- ASP 9mm (3D6).
- 5 attacks per combat round.
- +3 to strike, dodge, parry.
- +4 to initiative.

- 40 S.D.C.
- 40 Hit Points.

The riot armor that these officers are wearing is neck-to-toe armor, with their head being the only area that is exposed. The head is covered by a cloth mask, so that their identities cannot be determined. The officers will shoot first and ask questions later, so as soon as they are in the room initiative should be rolled.

Once the players dispatch with the officers they are free to search the bodies for any clues as to who sent them and why. The only information they will glean from this search is that they are all carrying security badges for the ConGenix corporate office in Albuquerque, New Mexico. This is a huge tip for the characters that ConGenix is one of the major antagonists in this campaign, which will set the players up to attempt an assault on the complex later. No other clues as to the motive of the attack can be gleaned from the officers.

At this point the characters may wish to do some research into ConGenix. Allow them to do so. They will be able to find out the following bits of information on successful Investigation or Research checks, or any other skill check that involves research:

- ConGenix is a multi-national corporation with its corporate headquarters in Albuquerque, New Mexico. The company was founded in 1985 as MilServe when the founder, Treondo Gonzalez, was awarded a contract to provide clothing services to the military. The company quickly expanded, and branched out into other areas of military services and research. The company currently provides weapons and technology to the military in the United States, England, Spain, France, Russia, and various other industrialized nations.
- According to public financial information, ConGenix is responsible for donating millions of dollars to the election campaigns of both Prio and Secoro Gonzalez.
- ConGenix has a state-of-the-art research facility located somewhere in the American Southwest, and it is rumored that they are working on everything from time travel to genetic modification.

Other non-important, public information can be made available to the players about the state of affairs at the company (they are publicly traded under the symbol CGNX, and the current price per share is $175.32), but nothing top-secret or damaging can be learned at this time. Any character asking questions about Treondo will learn that he is an identical triplet of Prio and Secoro; any character that figures this out without questioning should be awarded an extra 500 Experience Points.

While it is not designed to do so, the information the characters receive should alarm them. Why is a multi-national corporation sending armed officers to have them killed? Isn't it odd that the triplets are in the highest positions available? These questions cannot be answered now, and no information should be given to players who ask these questions.

The characters at this point may contact Lt. Draskal and inform them of what has happened, and what the outcome is. Lt. Draskal will inform them that he will take care of things, and that they should just get to a safe location so that the police can deal with it. He will do everything he can to make the players feel safe and that they are not going to be arrested. He will ask where they are going to go in the event he needs to contact them, and this is when he will strike.

As soon as the players are in a safe location, they are once again attacked by a team of ConGenix armed officers (6). These officers have the same stats as the officers the characters fought previously. This time, however, Lt. Draskal is leading the assault. It is the intention of Lt. Draskal to eliminate the characters, and these are the orders he has been given by his superiors at ConGenix. Lt. Draskal's stats:

Lt. Steven Draskal
3rd Level Experiment
Attributes: I.Q. 9, M.E. 12, M.A. 14, P.S. 17, P.P. 28, P.E. 9, P.B.: 10, Spd 15.
Hit Points: 15, **S.D.C.:** 79, **A.R.:** 4.
Combat: Attacks per Melee: 4
Damage: +2
Dodge: +11
Initiative: +2
Parry: +11
Pull: +3
Roll: +3
Strike: +9
Nature of the Experiment: Chemical and radiation combined.
Type of Experiment: Unexpected side effect of the experiment.
Side Effect: Mentally unstable.
- Reborn. Was originally a good cop, but the experimentation has turned him bad. Lt. Draskal will continue to pretend he is a good cop, although his motives are purely for the benefit of ConGenix.

Sponsoring Organization: Private Industry (ConGenix).
Status with the Sponsoring Organization: Currently employed by ConGenix (Chicago P.D. does not know this).
Minor Abilities:
Energy Expulsion: Light
- +3 to strike on aimed shot, +1 when shooting wild.
Indestructible Bones
Personal Force Field
- 48 S.D.C.
Scan Powers
Education: Trade School/On-The-Job-Training
Skill Program 1: Police, Basic Officer
- Athletics
- First Aid
- Hand to Hand: Expert
- Law
- Pilot: Automobile
- W.P. Pistol
- W.P. Shotgun

Skill Program 2: Police, Detective
- Bureaucracy
- Criminal Science
- Computer Operation
- Intelligence
- Interrogation
- Photography
- Police Procedures
- Research
- Streetwise

Secondary Skills (8)
- Advanced Mathematics
- Astronomy

- Basic Electronics
- Body Building & Weightlifting
- Prowl
- Running
- W.P. Revolver
- W.P. Submachine-Gun

He is wearing Riot Armor (A.R. 14, 180 S.D.C.), and is not carrying any weapons as he will use his Energy Expulsion power to fight the characters with. His Personal Force Field is up, and the S.D.C. of that will take damage first. While there is technically no A.R. for the force field, it is recommended to use the same A.R. as the riot armor. He will prefer to fight from the back of the room, allowing the armed officers to take the front line.

Lt. Draskal will not surrender, and he will not run. His orders are to either kill the characters or die trying. He knows that if he fails, he will be killed by his superiors at ConGenix.

If the characters do manage to capture Lt. Draskal, he will not answer any questions they may have unless they resort to torture (he gets a saving throw against a target of 15 for any question that is asked). If he makes his saving throw, he won't say anything other than to insult the characters. If he fails his saving throw, he will say that he is employed by ConGenix, and his orders are to kill them. The only thing he will say is that "He's coming for you. He won't let you get away with this." He won't say anything more, even if threatened with death. He will tell the characters that if they try to have him arrested it won't work, but the characters should figure this out on their own.

A search of the bodies will once again turn up security badges for ConGenix. If the characters kill Lt. Draskal, they will find a mini-computer on his person that contains a file detailing his orders to kill the characters. The order is signed by Treondo Gonzalez, and should lead the characters straight to ConGenix. The characters at this point should get the feeling that they need to do something about this corporation.

Just as the characters are starting to think about assaulting the corporation, they receive a telephone call from an anonymous person indicating that their lives are in danger. If questioned, the caller will say only that they need to watch out for "him," and that "he's coming for you – soon."

As soon as the phone call ends, the characters are assaulted by another team of armed officers from ConGenix (6). This time they are accompanied by Secoro Gonzalez, and he is not happy. The selected stats applicable for Secoro at this time are:

Hit Points: 53, **S.D.C.:** 47.
Combat: Attacks per Melee: 5
Damage: +2
Dodge: +1
Parry: +2
Pull: +2
Roll: +3
Save vs Insanity: +2
Save vs Psionics: +2

He is wearing a Hard Armor Vest (A.R. 12, 120 S.D.C.) over his 3-piece suit, and he is carrying a .44 magnum in a shoulder holster (6D6 damage).

Before the officers open fire on the players, Secoro informs them that he has taken it upon himself to make sure the players are eliminated. They are a menace to society, they have caused massive damage to the public, and they have (obviously) wiped out highly trained members of ConGenix's armed security force.

He wants to witness the players being killed – not arrested. At this, he instructs the armed forces to open fire, and they happily oblige.

This combat should go badly for Secoro and his guards. The point of this combat is for Secoro to either be outright killed, or hurt so badly that he will die soon. In the event he dies, the players should realize that they have just killed a member of Congress. This is not good news for the players, and they should know that they have to find a way to clear their names and prove that this was self-defense.

A possible outcome for this is that Secoro escapes, and this is fine. Should he be reduced to less than 20 Hit Points, he will immediately teleport away from harm, back to his office at ConGenix. If possible, he will run out of the room and teleport when the players are unable to see him.

Again, a search of the bodies turns up security badges for ConGenix. If they manage to kill Secoro, a search of his body turns up not only the badge but a scrap of paper in his wallet with the words "Celestial Base." The characters will not know what this means at this time, but they may be able to find out later.

Part II: Which Way Did They Go, George?

A day or so after the battle with Secoro, news stories start appearing in the newspaper (or at internet news sites, whichever the players are more apt to review) that should startle and worry the players. The following news stories can be read, but only one of them during any given day should be read:

DES MOINES – In what authorities are calling a very "shocking situation, with almost no explanation as to why," 27 year old Cary Franges, a Des Moines native all his life, has disappeared without a trace.

Authorities say that Franges, who is a school teacher by day and a karaoke DJ by night, was driving from his home to a local grocery store to do his shopping when he just disappeared. Authorities are unsure if he ever made it to the store as his car was found 4 blocks away, still running, but with very little gasoline left in the tank. A passerby called the police about the vehicle when she witnessed it sitting there, idling, for more than 30 minutes.

Police take the disappearance of any person very seriously, but this one takes on a new twist. Franges had just registered under Iowa's Super-Hero Registration Act a week ago. The abilities he registered include extremely sensitive hearing and the ability to control radioactive materials. Under the law, he was required to give his name, address, and employers.

Police have no suspects at this time.

WICHITA – Everybody wants to be able to enjoy their time away from work, and Jennifer Alberts was no different. Unfortunately for her, attempting to enjoy her time off has caused her to vanish into thin air.

Yesterday afternoon, Alberts, who was enjoying her first day off from work in over 3 weeks, went to McDonald Park to do a little jogging with her dog, and to catch a swim in one of the lakes, which friends say was one of her favorite activities. Witnesses say that both her and her dog, Muffin, jumped into the lake after their jog, but only Muffin came out. Jennifer, somehow, vanished.

Authorities have had the lake dredged to determine if her body had become entangled in some weeds or stuck in the mud, but her body has not yet been found. Family members say that she was an extremely strong swimmer, and that for her to drown is just a silly assumption. Until she can be found, alive or dead, the police have no choice but to assume the worst.

Alberts was registered under the "Powers" law here in Kansas, citing the ability to speak with fish and her strange ability to control plant life. When she registered, she stated that she just wanted to follow the laws of the state of Kansas, and was outspoken about having all super-heroes show that they are willing to work with law enforcement, and not against it.

DENVER – Nobody you know is supposed to be one. Not your mom, not your brother, not your best friend. But what about someone on TV? What about an athlete? Everybody knows them, right? This is why it was such a shock when Broncos running back Seth Radgar registered under the Heroes act. And it's also more shocking now that he's missing.

Everyone knows his story – 2 years ago, in Super Bowl LXVIII, Seth was the recipient of a pass from quarterback Jamie Danson, and proceeded to run 80 yards to score the winning touchdown. From there it was Super Bowl MVP, and then endorsement deals. After the Heroes act was passed, Seth came forward and admitted that he had abilities, which made it so he had to register, and his whole career was placed in jeopardy.

Under the law, he had to give the powers he had. Super speed. Unnatural strength. And the ability to actually pass through solid objects. And once he registered, everybody in the NFL, as well as the fans across the nation, cried foul. He was suspended by the league for cheating, and then eventually banned from play. He always stated that he wasn't required to tell the league at that time, but his complaints always fell on deaf ears.

And now, today, we've learned from his family and friends that he's been missing for a few days. He went out for a walk a few days ago, and he hasn't come back. Family and friends say that he's been depressed ever since being kicked out of the NFL, and that it's possible he may just be somewhere drowning his sorrows. Authorities are saying that they'll do everything they can to find him, but it doesn't appear that they are too eager to start doing that.

The above stories are designed to get the players' attention, and to get them thinking that super-heroes are starting to be abducted. You are free to invent your own news stories to show more super-heroes vanishing, and to drop any other hints you may think of to get the players to realize that foul play is on the menu.

At some point, the players are going to want to investigate one of the cities mentioned in the news stories to find out what they can about the disappearances. Any research performed remotely, i.e., on the internet, or by looking up information about the person abducted, will only give basic information. Players will be able to find out basic information about the city (information such as size, population, neighborhoods, etc.) or the person (name, address, powers listed under the registration act, etc.), but they will not be able to find out any more information regarding the abduction in this way. Even calling upon police contacts to investigate for them will glean nothing.

The only way to get any information is to go to one of the crime scenes and start poking around. This can be very dangerous for the players as they may be wanted by law enforcement AND they are going into a state with registration laws. It will be against the law for the players to be in that state for very long and not register, and while this shouldn't stop the players from going to that state, it should be stressed that their time there should be as short as possible. Unfortunately, their time wherever they decide to investigate is going to be a lot longer than they thought.

No matter which city they decide to investigate, their investigation will yield some or all of the following clues (it is up to you to decide which clues to give the players):

- The person abducted had more powers than the news story gave.
- The person abducted had powers that were extremely powerful, such as Control Radiation or APS Fire.
- A common thread among all abductees is that they all have powers that are highly dangerous.
- There is only 1 abductor (the players can determine this due to how quietly the people were abducted, especially those in broad daylight).
- The abductor might have super powers.

At the scene where they are investigating, the players will find a scrap of fabric with the corporate logo for ConGenix embroidered onto it. They should immediately question the involvement of ConGenix with the abduction, and why they are finding the corporate logo at the scene of the crime.

The players will also find at the scene a few globs of sticky fibers, similar to spider's webbing. This normally wouldn't be anything to alarm anyone, except that the globs are bigger than what one would normally see, and the fibers in the globs appear to be thicker and stronger than a normal spider's webbing.

The players will normally want to start asking questions of anybody in the surrounding area. As soon as they start to do this, they are interrupted by yet another minion of the corporate giant.

Zacharias "The Collector" Johannes
4th Level Eugenics
Attributes: I.Q. 15, M.E. 13, M.A. 6, P.S. 13, P.P. 28, P.E. 19, P.B. 8, Spd 36.
Hit Points: 49, **S.D.C.:** 154, **A.R.:** 15.
Combat: Attacks per Melee: 7
Auto-Dodge: +3
Dodge: +10
Disarm: +1
Initiative: +4
Parry: +11
Pull: +5
Roll: +5
Strike: +7
Save vs Coma/Death: +42%
Save vs Disease: +1

Save vs Drugs: +5
Save vs Heart/Blood Diseases: +4
Save vs Magic: +5
Save vs Poison: +11
Save vs Psionics: +3
Save vs Toxins: +8
Current Status with the Sponsoring Organization: Good standing. Currently employed by ConGenix as an assassin, and is used to abduct/retrieve super heroes for the Moon Prison.
Sponsoring Organization: ConGenix.
Motive for Genetic Reconstruction: Criminal.
Conditions of Eugenic Modification: Healthy Volunteer.
Budget Amount: $11 million.
Purchased Parts and Abilities
Adhesion. Cost: $500,000.
Ambidextrous. Cost: $300,000.
Appendix, Modified. Cost: $400,000.
Attribute Enhancement, Physical Endurance, 10x. Cost: $2,500,000.
Bio-Regeneration, Healing Factor. Cost: $1,200,000.
Brain, Combat/Motor Head. Cost: $700,000.
Chemical Secretion, Sleep. Cost: $450,000.
Digestive System Enhancement. Cost: $300,000.
Gills, Chimera. Cost: $400,000.
Gland, Melatonin. Cost: $200,000.
Heart. Cost: $650,000.
Natural Armor Rating, Heavy. Cost: $2,500,000.
Needle Blossom (35 each forearm, 18 in chest). Cost: $300,000.
Spinnerets. Cost: $500,000.
Spinnerets Enhancement. Cost: $100,000.
Total Cost: **$11,000,000**
Bonus Skills
- Climbing
- W.P. Paired Weapons

Education: 2 Years of College/Trade School – Con Artist
Skill Program 1: Rogue, Con Man
- Concealment
- Disguise
- Forgery
- Palming
- Pick Pocket
- Shell Game
- Streetwise: Con Games

Skill Program 2: Rogue, Professional Thief
- Climbing
- Demolitions
- Hot-Wiring
- Locksmith
- Prowl
- Read Sensory Equipment
- Safe-Cracking
- Surveillance Systems

Skill Program 3: Rogue, Black Marketeer
- Accounting
- Appraisal
- Bargain/Bribe
- Find Contraband
- Locate Secret Compartments
- Pilot: Automobile

- Recognize Weapon Quality
- Streetwise
- Streetwise: Drugs
- W.P. Auto Pistol

Skill Program 4: Basic, Fitness Specialist
- Athletics
- Body Building
- Hand to Hand: Basic
- Meditation
- Running

10 Secondary Skills
- Art
- Card Sharp
- Electronics: Basic
- First Aid
- Mechanics: Basic
- Pick Locks
- Radio: Basic
- Seduction
- T.V. & Video
- Ventriloquism

Zacharias is a criminal, no doubt about it. Because of his eugenic modifications, he is under contract to provide certain services to ConGenix, one of these services being to abduct those with super-powers and bring them back to the ConGenix laboratory located in Albuquerque, New Mexico. He has become known as "The Collector" as he is very good at what he does.

He arrives on the scene by dropping literally out of the sky a short distance away from the players. He is dressed entirely in black, except for his forearms and the central part of his chest, between his neck and his breastbone. These two areas are uncovered so he can make use of his needle blossoms if he has to. He also has the ConGenix logo tattooed on the underside of this left forearm; again, this is one of his contractual obligations.

Zacharias is not concerned with killing the characters, only capturing one of them. Whichever player appears to have the most dangerous super ability is the one he is targeting. He will attempt to entangle his target with his webbing, while at the same time using his sleep chemical to cause all of the players to fall asleep. Players are allowed a saving throw vs poisons or toxins, whichever allows the higher bonus. Players who fail their saving throw are rendered incapacitated for 1D6 melee rounds, while those who make their saving throw are still awake but lose 2 actions due to being groggy.

Zacharias will not attempt to use the needle blossom unless the fight is going really badly for him. This is a last ditch effort to incapacitate opponents, as he generally shoots the needles from his forearms and/or chest into the eyes of his opponents when necessary. Any player actually hit is effectively blinded for 1D6 melee rounds, and suffers all of the same effects as being blinded.

It is entirely possible that the players could become rendered unconscious, only to awaken to find their comrade missing. This is actually a good scenario, as this will force the players to mount an assault on ConGenix, which after this fight should be the next logical step taken by the players anyhow. The abducted player will be found at the Moon Prison later in the campaign (see Part III: Home Sweet Home Away From Home).

It is possible that the players may capture Zacharias. Unfortunately for the players, Zacharias is unable to talk as he had his larynx removed during the eugenic modification procedure. This was actually one of his stipulations to becoming an employee of ConGenix; if he is to be silent, the best way is to not speak. In this scenario, all the players will learn is that ConGenix is behind the attack (thanks to the tattoo on Zacharias' left forearm). This is the same amount of information the players will learn if they kill Zacharias.

At this point, the players should really not like ConGenix. In fact, they should feel more than a little animosity towards the corporation. And it is at this point where the characters should start to get the idea that they may need to confront the corporation and attempt to take it out. Cultivate these feelings in the players, and if necessary steer them towards this goal. The player's next step should be to go after the corporation, and you are free to plant any adventure hooks or clues between the city they are currently in and Albuquerque to get them there.

Before the players mount an assault on the company, they should be at least between 3rd and 4th level, with being at 4th or even 5th level optimal. Feel free to run any side adventures you like to get the players up to this level. Once they are at the appropriate level, they can begin their assault on the company.

Traveling to Albuquerque may be a bit difficult for the characters. Thanks to the national media, they are currently wanted for questioning regarding the deaths of Percy Harrison and Steven Draskal. Furthermore, several states between Illinois and New Mexico have enacted super-hero registration laws (Missouri, Kansas, Oklahoma, Texas, Colorado, and New Mexico all have registration laws), so travelling through these states is going to be tricky. The characters will need to take conventional means of travel, and will probably need to disguise themselves in order to get to Albuquerque unnoticed.

It will take approximately 2 days to get from Chicago to Albuquerque (more or less time may be needed depending on where the players go to investigate the disappearances) via car, truck, or van, and the players will need to stop at least once in every state they pass through for gasoline. When they do, there is a chance (01-35%, +20% if they are not disguised in any way) that they are recognized for who they truly are. If they are recognized, local law enforcement will be called to the scene, and the players may need to find a way around dealing with the police. Use the same stats given during the Daley Center incident for any police officers that may show up.

Traveling by airplane is not an option for the players. They will have to make their way through TSA at any airport they wish to use, and giving their identification to a TSA official will immediately alert airport security that the players are there. It should be stressed to the players that using the airport is not a good idea. If they do, however, continue to want to use the airport, use the weather as an excuse that flights are delayed. Do not let the players fly (unless, of course, they have the applicable super ability to fly unaided).

While they are en route to Albuquerque, they will have the distinct privilege of seeing, on television, an interview that should be of great interest to them, given by Secoro Gonzalez:

> "I want to start first by saying my family and I appreciate all of the sentiments and heart-felt wishes for health that have come from everyone here and across this great nation. It warms my soul to know that I am not alone in this time of need.

> "The attack that I suffered at the hands of these super-powered criminals only shows that they cannot be trusted. Power, in any form, in the hands of those who are evil at heart will only be used to further their own evil thoughts, schemes, and plans. And it is for this reason that I have amended the Super-Hero Registration bill to not only force super-powered beings to register, but to make the use of those powers illegal, except in times of national defense.

> "I have been asked to give details about the attack. All I can say at this time is that I was assaulted in a variety of ways, and that the criminals are still at large. My only wish is to see them arrested and brought to justice."

This interview should seriously alarm the characters, especially if they killed Secoro. If he is dead, then how can he possibly be on television giving an interview about the attack? Players are already aware that ConGenix is using super-powered individuals to hunt them down, and now they should be wondering if the people at the top aren't super-powered individuals too.

ConGenix is located at 650 Haines Ave NW, on the site of the former National Research Labs, Inc. NRLI was purchased by ConGenix as a way for ConGenix to expand into computer and circuit board manufacturing. The players should be able to find the building quite easily, but getting in may be a different story.

The easiest way to enter the building is through the front door. However, doing so will mean the players are unable to get anywhere into the building beyond the lobby as they will be stopped immediately.

A second option is to enter the building through the roof, but this is not a viable option. The roof access leads directly to a security station with no less than 4 armed officers (use the same stats as the officers that attacked the players in Chicago), and the players will be in for quite the shock when during the first round of combat a contingent of another 20 or so officers makes their way into the security station. How is this possible so quickly? The rooftop access door is wired to set off a silent alarm, registered by all officers in the complex, in the event the door is opened from the outside.

A third option would be to teleport or phase-shift into the building. This option is not possible as the building is magically protected to prevent the use of super-powers to enter the building. Teleporting, phase-shifting, invisibility, chameleon, etc., will not work. The players will need to enter through either the front door or the rooftop door, in full view of the cameras. This magical protection includes preventing people from using these abilities to move about once they are in the building, but it can be disabled (see Part IV: Haven't We Done This Already?), allowing them to use these powers.

A map/floor plan of the building is not given here, but is instead given later when the players will attempt to assault the corporate giant a second time (see Part IV: Haven't We Done This Already?). This is because the players will not get very far into the building this time, but during the next assault they will get deep into the building and potentially destroy it. The map is given then to save space.

All in all, the assault on the building is designed to go badly. No matter which way they use to get into the building, let them in, but do not allow them to go beyond either the lobby (through the front doors) or the security office (through the rooftop access door). If they go in through the front door, security is alerted and they are greeted by the contingent of 20 officers. Entering through the roof will result in the same thing.

The players should get the impression that they are not going to win this fight. If the players wish to fight it out until the officers are dead, then so be it. Once the officers are down to less than 50% of their original number, another contingent of 20 officers is called in for back-up. Repeat this until the players get the hint.

The players will not be able to escape due to the sheer number of officers in the area, and they won't be able to leave using super powers. Eventually the players will see that they cannot win and should wish to open talks with the officers. When this happens, read the following:

> *One of the armed security guards approaches, stopping a few feet in front of you. He takes off his riot mask, and you can see that he looks exactly like Lt. Steven Draskal. He has the same haircut, same eyes, and same shape. But when he speaks, you can tell that his voice is different, and this is not the lieutenant.*
>
> *"Not sure what you guys thought you were going to accomplish assaulting the building, but you've got guts. Unfortunately for you, guts isn't enough.*
>
> *"The lot of you are criminals, wanted in connection with at least a dozen deaths in Chicago, to include Percy Harri-*

> *son and Steven Draskal. You are also wanted for questioning in the disappearances of several individuals in more than a couple different states.*
>
> *"You guys are facing multiple federal offenses and several state violations, and because of that I have orders to have you arrested and detained until you can be turned over to the proper authorities. Will you comply with these orders?"*

The players shouldn't want to be arrested at this point, but they have no choice. They are surrounded by many armed guards, all in riot gear and pointing automatic weapons at them. It is possible that one or more of the players is a seemingly unstoppable juggernaut, but that shouldn't cause them to start attacking at this point. Remind the players that there are security cameras inside the building, and that their actions are being recorded. If they do wish to continue the attack, continue with combat and keep sending in reinforcements.

Eventually, the players should get the hint and allow themselves to be arrested. When the players agree to be arrested, they are handcuffed, and then given an injection designed to knock them out completely. If any of the players is immune to poison, then that player is knocked into unconsciousness either by physical force (a nightstick to the back of the head) or by psionics. Either way, all of the players are rendered unconscious just after being arrested.

If the players subdue/kill any of the guards, award them the appropriate Experience Points for doing so. If they are arrested without harming any of the guards, award each player 500 Experience Points for showing intellect and not just wantonly wading into combat against terrible odds.

Part III: Home Sweet Home Away from Home

Eventually, the players will wake up from their drug (or magic/psionic/physical force) induced unconsciousness. When they wake, read them the following:

> *You wake up in what you have come to know as your home – a rather large prison cell, with a few other inmates. You are all dressed in green jumpsuits, with flip-flops for shoes. Your hair is greasy, you are starting to itch from the fleas and other bugs, and you're hungry even though you know that the food here sucks worse than hospital food.*
>
> *You sit up in bed, your head still swimming from being forced to work so hard for so many hours every single day. You rack your brain, trying to remember why it is that your life is so messed up; you try to remember why you are in this place, and for what crime it is that you are paying with your life. And then it comes to you, slowly at first, as if out of a dense fog, the choppy memories that remind you why you are here.*
>
> *Murder. You are a murderer, and you have been sentenced to life without parole in this rotten prison. You try to remember the details of your trial, but they mostly elude you. You are able to piece together bits of your trial, which seem to involve a lot of police officers being angry with you, and some type of business person giving a lot of testimony and evidence against you. But the harder you try to remember exactly what happened, the more you realize that it is impossible to do so.*
>
> *You stretch out over the bed, hoping to get a grip on yourself and stop your head from swimming, but you can't. Something is nagging at you, telling you that you are different from all of these other people in here, but you can't put your finger on what it is. You hang your head over the edge of the bed and see your reflection in the water in a bucket next to you.*
>
> *Normal. Completely normal. Normal eyes, normal hair, normal face. Nothing about you is out of the ordinary, or different. You are just an average person, in a world of average people, serving out a life sentence for murder.*
>
> *You get to your feet and realize that the day is about to begin, and that the guards will be coming to drag you off to the work pens soon. You've got to get your senses about you, or you'll be punished. Again.*

The players, after having been arrested at ConGenix, have been detained at a prison designed specifically for the incarceration of super-powered beings. Their memories have been altered to prevent them from remembering most of what transpired prior to their jailing, as well as to prevent them from knowing that they themselves are super-powered beings.

So how is this done? A device known simply as the Crown, which is essentially an electronic ring the diameter of a person's head and 3 inches high, has been placed upon each of the player's heads. This device transmits electronic signals into the brain of whoever wears it, altering their memories and behavior as the controller sees fit. The controller is a person who operates the computer that all Crowns are linked to, and this computer station is kept inside the prison (see the prison details below for a description of where the computer station/controller is).

In the case of the inmates at this prison, which is affectionately called "Hell-Box 99," or "99," the Crown alters the memories by blocking real ones and implanting memories designed to keep the inmates believing they are in prison for life for a heinous, violent crime. Target memories produce specific electronic signals, and when these signals are picked up by the Crown they can be dampened, preventing the person from remembering what truly happened. This is especially effective into making the inmates believe that they are not super-powered beings, as memories of their powers and abilities are dampened, preventing them from trying to use them.

The real problem with the Crown is that one of the signals it sends into the brain is a concealment mechanism for itself. Anybody wearing the Crown is unable to feel it on their own heads, feel it with their hands, or see it on someone else or in their own reflections. Although electronic, it is perfectly waterproof, has a Natural A.R. of 12, and 75 S.D.C.

The Crown is also designed to be used as a controlling mechanism over those who wear it. All Crowns in the prison are linked to a central control computer, guarded and watched over by members of the staff. On the orders of any staff member, the computer can send out a signal to one or any number of active Crowns that tells the Crown to send a strong electrical impulse into the mind of the inmate. This electrical impulse has one purpose – to completely disable the inmate. Any such shock received by an inmate (or by one of the players) is crippling, forcing the inmate to his or her knees and writhing in pain. The effect is similar to the minor super ability *Mental Stun*, with the added bonus that those who fail their savings throws are completely incapacitated for 1D6 melee rounds. Those who make their saving throws suffer the effects listed on page 235 of *Heroes Unlimited™, 2ⁿᵈ Edition* for the super ability as if they had failed their saving throw.

It locks into place by magnetism – 4 small magnets are implanted into the head of the person who will be wearing the device, and the device is then magnetically stuck to the person's head. It takes a P.S. of at least 22 to remove the device when in proper working order due to the strength of the magnets holding it in place. When not functioning properly, the device can just simply be slipped off the head.

The prison is modeled after the Leistikow Strasse (pronounced LY-stih-kow STRAH-seh) prison in Potsdam, Germany, which is about 20 miles southwest of Berlin. All of the details about Leistikow Strasse were preserved when the prison was built, which means that the cells are medium sized (about 10 x 10), with each one housing approximately 5 prisoners. As the prisoners are either working 16 hour days, eating, or sleeping, all that is in the cells are beds.

The ground floor of the prison is used primarily for housing those inmates in general population, as well as serving as the prison reception area for new arrivals. There is a communal shower/toilet area in the southeast corner of the floor, as well as a security station near the entrance to the prison. The stairs in the south portion of the ground floor go up to the second floor, while the stairs in the east portion go both up to the second floor and down to the basement.

The upper floor of the prison serves three purposes. The first is to house new inmates until the appropriate "paperwork" has been completed on them and they are assigned either to general population or the basement facilities. The second purpose is to prepare the food and drink the inmates and staff will consume, with a kitchen in the southeast portion of the level. The staff of the prison eats in the kitchen in shifts, while all prisoners eat their meals either in their cells or in the work areas that they are assigned to.

The third purpose of the upper level is to force inmates to work on various projects that are, invariably, designed to keep them more secure in the prison than they already are. There are a total of 5 workshops on the upper level, each with a different purpose. Inmates will be involved in any number of differing projects, all designed to either provide additional security for the prison (prisoners' memories are modified to prevent them from figuring out what the project is for), or to export some products so the facility can make a profit.

The basement level is the real horror of the prison. Those prisoners that are deemed suitable for incarceration in the basement level face a reality that is unlike any other. Most of the rooms in the basement level house strange devices that are designed to draw power from super-powered beings and use it to power all of the other faculties of the prison.

The devices are similar to giant snow globes – transparent globes that a super-powered being is contained in, with electrical wiring and cabling running between it and various outlets in the wall. Super-powered beings are held captive in these devices and kept continuously unconscious, their powers being sucked out of them forcibly to power the rest of the prison. Only those super-powered beings with extremely dangerous powers – APS Fire/Plasma, Control Radiation, Energy Expulsion, etc. – are kept here. Each of the rooms in the basement house at least 3 of these globes, all with a super-powered being in them.

The kicker to this prison is that it is not in the United States, nor is it anywhere on Earth, for that matter. The prison is actually situated on the moon, and there is a shuttle service to and from the prison for the transport of prisoners, staff, products, and other various items. The shuttle bay can house 2 shuttles at once, although it is rare that any more than 1 shuttle is in the bay at one time. The only way to get to the shuttle bay is to go through the 2-way teleporter (see the detailed map and corresponding room descriptions for details).

When the players wake, they will undoubtedly have questions: How did they get there, where they are exactly, what happened during their trials, etc.? Let them ask – they will get no answers here at the prison. All they will be told no matter who they ask – staff or other inmates – is that they are in prison for committing a crime, and that they should do their best to just serve their sentence peacefully.

Although they won't know this now, the prison is owned and operated by our favorite corporate powerhouse, ConGenix. The players will have the opportunity to find this information out later, and it will drive them towards the goal of taking out the corporate giant in Part IV: Haven't We Done This Already?

Players will probably also attempt to use any super-powers they may have to try and escape the prison. While they are still wearing the Crown, they will not know they have any super-powers, and you may have to remind them of the fact that they firmly believe that they do not have any super-powers. This portion of the campaign will rely heavily on role-playing, research, and investigative capabilities. For that matter, all Experience Point awards in the prison except for confrontations with the staff during the inevitable escape should be doubled.

Surprisingly enough, and as a cruel and twisted joke by the staff and ConGenix officials, inmates who are not confined to the power globes in the basement will be assigned to some type of work detail that is actually related to whatever super-powers they may have. For example, a person who has the ability of Toy Control will be working in a makeshift toy workshop. The staff at the prison takes great pleasure in knowing that the inmates are forced to work with the one thing that they are closest to without even knowing it.

The stats to use for any security personnel in the prison are as follows:
- Full suit of Riot Armor (A.R. 14, 180 S.D.C.).
- A .45 M3 (4D6).
- ASP 9mm (3D6).
- Some (01-10%) may have Stakeout Ithacan Shotgun (4D6) instead of the .45 M3.
- 5 attacks per melee round.
- +3 to strike, dodge, parry.
- +4 to initiative.
- 40 S.D.C.
- 40 Hit Points.

All of the guards will have patches on the upper left arm of their riot gear that is emblazoned with the corporate logo of ConGenix.

1. This is the entrance into the prison. There are never any guards on duty in this room as it is not expected that anyone will try to escape from the prison. Furthermore, when new inmates or dignitaries arrive, their arrival is announced ahead of time, and guards can be stationed in this room to wait for them.

The door that leads to this room is actually a 2-way teleporter that leads directly to the shuttle bay (Prison Map 4, room 67). The wall to the south is an illusionary wall designed to prevent inmates from escaping. When viewed from this area, the wall appears to be a shimmering mirror, allowing viewers to see into the next room. To enter the next room, one only has to walk through the wall.

2. This is the central intake station. All new inmates will pass through this area, where a security guard will take a sample of their DNA for further processing. Inmates are generally unconscious when they arrive, so they will have no memory of this ever happening. Two security guards are stationed here at all times, usually sitting at a desk on the western wall.

The wall to the north is an illusionary wall designed to prevent inmates from escaping. When viewed from this area, it appears to be just another wall with the same look as the rest of the walls in the prison. Anyone wearing a Crown when viewing this wall will automatically fail a saving throw vs magic and be unable to discern that something is wrong with the wall. Anyone not wearing a Crown when viewing this wall is allowed a saving throw

vs magic at a target of 15, with success indicating that the wall is not real.

The wall is a permanent magical enchantment, created by the spell *Circle of Concealment*.

3. This is the central security station for the prison. This room houses all of the security computers and connections to the security cameras throughout the prison. All inmate information, as well as information about the prison is housed in computers in this room.

On the west wall of the room is a gun locker containing 6 7.62 mm rifles (4D6) and 600 rounds of ammunition for the rifles. In a chest next to the locker are 3 riot jackets (A.R. 10, 60 S.D.C. each) and 3 concealed vests (A.R. 10, 50 S.D.C. each). The room

will always have 4 security guards inside monitoring prison activities.

This area also houses the central computer that controls all of the Crowns in use at the prison. With a simple command, the computer can send out a signal to any or all Crowns to mentally stun and incapacitate an inmate.

4. This is one of 4 barracks areas in the prison, all of which are located on the ground floor. The room contains beds to sleep 5 guards (who sleep in shifts), as well as lockers and chests where guards can put their effects (weapons, armor, clothing, etc.) for safekeeping while they sleep. At any given time, there will be 4 guards asleep in this room. It will take them 1 melee round to awaken, and another melee round to don their riot armor.

5. This is one of 4 barracks areas in the prison, all of which are located on the ground floor. The room contains beds to sleep 5 guards (who sleep in shifts), as well as lockers and chests where guards can put their effects (weapons, armor, clothing, etc.) for safekeeping while they sleep. At any given time, there will be 4 guards asleep in this room. It will take them 1 melee round to awaken, and another melee round to don their riot armor.

6. This is one of 4 barracks areas in the prison, all of which are located on the ground floor. The room contains beds to sleep 8 guards (who sleep in shifts), as well as lockers and chests where guards can put their effects (weapons, armor, clothing, etc.) for safekeeping while they sleep. At any given time, there will be 4 guards asleep in this room. It will take them 1 melee round to awaken, and another melee round to don their riot armor.

7. This is one of 4 barracks areas in the prison, all of which are located on the ground floor. The room contains beds to sleep 8 guards (who sleep in shifts), as well as lockers and chests where guards can put their effects (weapons, armor, clothing, etc.) for safekeeping while they sleep. At any given time, there will be 4 guards asleep in this room. It will take them 1 melee round to awaken, and another melee round to don their riot armor.

8. This stairwell only goes in one direction – up. This is one of the two stairwells in the building that allow access to the upper floor (to room 30).

9. This is the central hallway of the ground floor. Like the rest of the prison, it is well lit and has multiple cameras to catch all angles. There are always 6 guards in this area: 2 outside of each of the stairwells (rooms 8 and 18), 1 guard patrolling the portion of the hall running east to west, and 1 guard patrolling the portion of the hall running north to south.

10. One of the cells used to house prisoners. The cell sleeps 5 inmates, and has only beds. It is in this cell that the players will awaken.

11. One of the cells used to house prisoners. The cell sleeps 10 inmates, and has only beds. At any given time, there will be 4 inmates in this cell.

12. One of the cells used to house prisoners. The cell sleeps 5 inmates, and has only beds. At any given time, there will be 2 inmates in this cell.

13. One of the cells used to house prisoners. The cell sleeps 7 inmates, and has only beds. At any given time, there will be 3 inmates in this cell.

14. One of the cells used to house prisoners. The cell sleeps 10 inmates, and has only beds. At any given time, there will be 4 inmates in this cell.

15. One of the cells used to house prisoners. The cell sleeps 20 inmates, and has only beds. At any given time, there will be 8 inmates in this cell.

16. One of the cells used to house prisoners. The cell sleeps 10 inmates, and has only beds. At any given time, there will be 4 inmates in this cell.

17. One of the cells used to house prisoners. The cell sleeps 10 inmates, and has only beds. At any given time, there will be 4 inmates in this cell.

18. The only stairwell that has multiple directions. This set of stairs allows access to the upper floor much like the stairs in room 8 (to room 39), and it is the only stairwell that allows access to the basement level (to room 66). The door to these stairs is the only door on the ground floor that is locked.

19. This is an area used by guards to keep an eye on inmates who are using the communal shower and toilet area.

20. This is the communal shower and toilet area for the ground floor of the prison. The only way to gain access to this area is through the stairwell (room 18), which means that a guard must accompany the inmate into the area. The door to the stairs from the hallway is locked, which means a guard has to unlock the door for the inmate to gain access. This is not only a measure to insure that the inmates don't get down to the basement, but also to make sure that the inmates are behaving themselves in the shower.

At any given time, there may be (01-30%) 1D4+1 inmates in the shower area. If there are any inmates in the shower area, there will always be 1 guard in room 19.

21. This is a storeroom designed to house some necessities used by the prisoners – soap, shampoo, toilet paper, towels, etc.

22. One of 5 workshops on the upper level, this one is used for electrical projects. Wiring, cabling, and other electrical/electronic components can all be found in this room, with various projects all in various stages of completion. Any tools necessary to work on these projects can be found here as well. At any time there will be 1D10+1 inmates and 1 guard in this workshop.

23. One of 5 workshops on the upper level, this one is used for computer projects. Monitors, disk drives, keyboards, and other computer parts can be found all over the room, with various projects in various stages of completion. Any tools necessary to work on these projects can be found here as well. At any time there will be 1D10+1 inmates and 1 guard in this workshop.

24. One of the 5 workshops on the upper level, this one is used for metalworking. Steel lathes, drills, presses, and minor smelting facilities can be found in the room, with various projects in various stages of completion. Any tools necessary to work on these projects can be found here as well. At any time there will be 1D10+1 inmates and 1 guard in this workshop.

25. The smallest of the 5 workshops, this one is used for woodworking. Lathes, drills, saws, sanders, hammers, screwdrivers, and other woodworking tools can be found here, with various projects in various stages of completion. This is the smallest shop in the prison as there isn't much of a demand to make products out of wood. At any time there will be 1D4+1 inmates and 1 guard in this workshop.

26. One of the 5 workshops on the upper level, this one is used for plastics. Lathes, drills, presses, and machines to create plastic can be found in the room, with various projects in various stages of completion. Any tools necessary to work on these projects can be found here as well. At any time there will be 1D10+1 inmates and 1 guard in this workshop.

27. This is the central security area for the upper floor. A circular work station is in the middle of the area, and there are always 3 guards at this station. Two other guards are always patrolling the remainder of the hallway, one from north to south and the other from east to west.

28. This is a small room used as a security pass-through from the upper level to the lower level. All inmates who pass through this room are subjected to a search of their person to insure that they haven't attempted to take any tools from the workshops back to their cells. There is always 1 guard on duty in this room.

29. This is a small, empty room that appears to have once been used as a closet or broom cupboard. The door in the south wall that allows access to room 31 is actually a secret door that can only be found by someone who is actively searching for it. The appropriate skill is *Detect Concealment*, and players will need to make a check against this skill with a -30% penalty as the mechanism to operate the door is in the ceiling near the exit to room 27.

30. This is a set of stairs that allows access back to the ground floor (room 8).

31. This is a hidden room used to store items taken from inmates when they arrive. Items such as magical and normal weapons, power armor, alien technology, etc., are all stored here until they can be researched fully (and potentially used by the guards at the prison).

While the room looks small on the map, it is actually an extra-dimensional space created with a magic ritual. There are no limits to the size of the room, and anyone who enters will immediately know that the room is much bigger than what the architecture of the building should allow.

32. This area is a storage room that houses the medical supplies used in room 33. Bandages, gauze, sutures, forceps, etc., can all be found here, as well as other medications and drugs used to treat various illnesses and diseases.

33. This area is the medical room, and is used to treat those inmates who have fallen ill or who have been roughed up by the security guards for one reason or another. While a Crown can alter a person's memories, it cannot heal them of injuries sustained. And there is no professionally trained doctor on staff; the nurse who can always be found in this room when not eating received her training on the job working for her now-deceased mob boyfriend Lorenzo "Left Leg" Lassuario. She would often have to patch him up after he spent time out with the boys. Her applicable skills are:

- First Aid (65%)
- Holistic Medicine (65%)
- Paramedic (60%)

Anyone brought to her has a decent chance of receiving the appropriate medical care, even for severe injuries such as burns or broken bones. First aid normally doesn't cover the full treatment of these types of injuries, but with her background the nurse is more than capable of using this skill to treat people.

34. This is one of the 4 rooms on the upper floor used to house new inmates who are awaiting permanent placement within the prison. The room is furnished the same as the cells on the ground floor, and house up to 10 inmates. At any time, 1D10 inmates will be in this room.

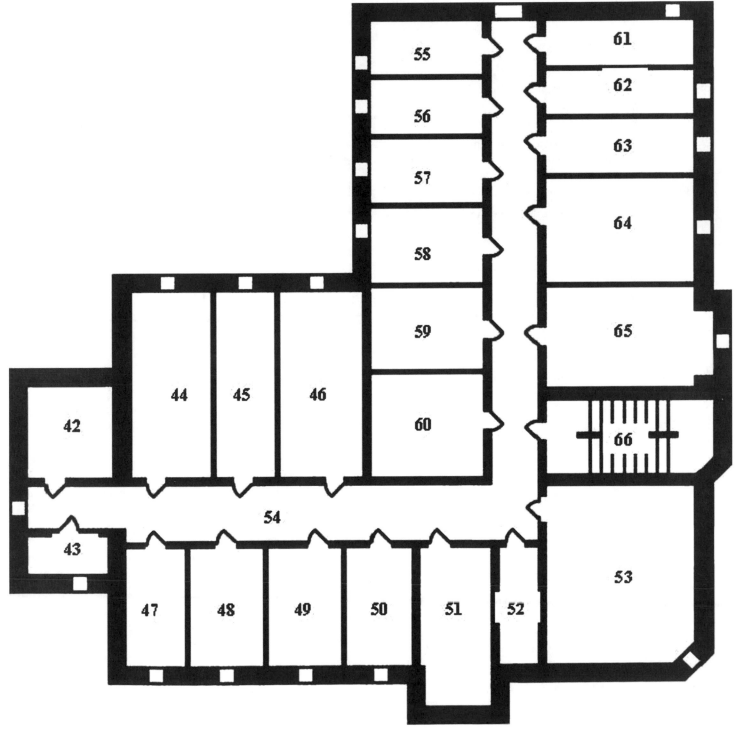

35. This is a confinement cell for any inmates in the prison who have been deemed as being a danger to themselves, other inmates, or the staff. And although the room is designed to only hold 1 inmate, there have been times where up to 5 inmates have been crammed into this cell. When prisoners are confined to this cell, the door is locked. Presently, no inmates are confined to this cell.

36. This is one of the 4 rooms on the upper floor used to house new inmates who are awaiting permanent placement within the prison. The room is furnished the same as the cells on the ground floor, and house up to 20 inmates. At any time, 1D10 inmates will be in this room.

37. This is one of the 4 rooms on the upper floor used to house new inmates who are awaiting permanent placement within the prison. The room is furnished the same as the cells on the ground floor, and house up to 20 inmates. At any time, 1D10 inmates will be in this room.

38. This is one of the 4 rooms on the upper floor used to house new inmates who are awaiting permanent placement within the prison. The room is furnished the same as the cells on the ground floor, and house up to 20 inmates. At any time, 1D10 inmates will be in this room.

39. This set of stairs allows access to the ground floor much like the stairs in room 30 (to room 18), as well as allowing access to the basement level (to room 66). The door to these stairs is one of two doors on the upper floor that can be locked.

40. This is an area used by guards to keep an eye on inmates who have been assigned to kitchen duty and are currently working to prepare meals.

41. This is the kitchen area of the prison. All meals are prepared and cooked here by inmates who have been assigned to kitchen duty, and this is also where the security guards prefer to eat their meals. At any given time, there will be 1D4+2 inmates in the kitchen working to prepare meals, as well as 1 guard in area 40 watching over them.

With the exception of the power room (area 53), the hall (area 54), and the stairs (area 66), all rooms in the basement have the following description:

> *Each of these rooms houses the true horror of the prison: large, transparent globes that hold super-powered beings, sucking their powers out of them. Cabling and wires stretch from the globes to transformers near the walls, changing the super ability energy into power that can be used to power the whole prison. The rooms are dark, save for small emissions of light from tiny electrical charges running over the surface of each globe.*

Each of the rooms can hold a different number of these globes. The following list shows how many globes are in each room.

2 globes – area 43
3 globes – areas 42, 52
5 globes – areas 47, 48, 49, 50, 55, 56, 57, 61, 62, 63
7 globes – areas 44, 45, 46, 51, 58, 59, 60, 64, 65

Overall, the prison makes use of 121 globes to power the prison. All of the globes have an inmate in them, each with a different high-powered super ability that gives off some type of energy or heat.

53. This is the power room for the prison. All energy collected from the inmates housed in the globes is transferred to huge storage tanks contained in this room, and the power is then sent to the areas of the prison that need it, to include the shuttle bay area. Three guards will always be on duty in this area, watching over the computers that show the power levels and the security measures in place to house the inmates in the globes.

54. This is the central hallway that allows access to all rooms/areas in the basement level. There are always 2 guards on duty here, one patrolling from north to south and one patrolling from east to west.

66. This is the set of stairs that allows access back up to the ground floor (area 18) as well as the upper floor (area 39). The door to this set of stairs is locked, and is guarded by 2 guards who are stationed just outside the door in the hallway (area 54).

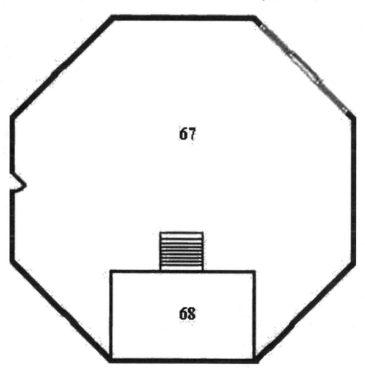

67. This is the central launching area for the shuttle bay. The bay itself is large enough to hold 2 shuttles at once, but launching and landing would be extremely difficult. There is always one shuttle in the bay in the event of emergencies, and the shuttle is pre-programmed with launch instructions and a flight path directly back to ConGenix in Albuquerque, NM.

The door that leads into the shuttle bay is actually a 2-way dimensional teleporter between the shuttle bay and the front reception area (Prison Map 1, room 1). Shuttles land and take off through the shielded window in the northeast corner, which gives a spectacular view of the moon and the stars.

68. Up a small flight of stairs from the shuttle bay is a platform that is used for coordinating launching and landing of shuttles. A bank of computers and terminals allows for the control of the shielded window, as well as being able to communicate with the shuttles when in flight. When the shielded window is retracted to allow for flights to land and/or take off, the entire area is shielded from the effects of the vacuum of space by the equivalent of the super ability *Create Force Field*, except that air and other gases cannot pass through the force field. It has an effective A.R. of 10 and 1,000 S.D.C.

When the players wake up, they will find themselves in area 10 on the ground floor of the prison. Any player who was captured by the eugenics assassin in Part II will awaken in area 35 on the upper floor, and will then almost immediately thereafter be taken by 2 guards down the stairs in area 39 to the ground floor and thrown unceremoniously into the cell with the other players (area 10). Only the players will ever be in this cell – no other inmates will ever use this cell to eat, sleep, or wile away the time.

Once awake, players will be forced into a very specific routine at the prison: they wake up, they are allowed to shower, they eat, they go to work in one of the workshops, they are brought back to their cells, and they sleep. This routine will make the players sick, but it is the one that they are responsible for following for the time being. In due time, things will pick up.

Should any of the players start asking questions about where they are, or why they are there, or that they want to speak to their lawyer, the guards in the security room (area 3 on the ground floor) will activate the computer and have the Crown on that player disable/incapacitate him. Remember that players who make their saving throws are still subjected to the same effects for the super ability *Mental Stun* as if they had failed their saving throw, while actually failing the saving throw results in being completely incapacitated for 4D6 melee rounds (1D6 minutes). This usually results in unconsciousness, and the guards will continue to have the player's mind zapped until he does pass out.

The players should be allowed to talk to one another while they are in their cell, but they will have no recollection of any interactions they had previously, and will speak as though they are meeting for the first time. They can ask for names, and what they are incarcerated for (in all cases it will be a violent crime of some kind), what their sentence is (in all cases it is life in prison), and what shop they work in (depending on their actual super abilities, the exact shop should be determined by the G.M.).

After the players settle into this routine, strange things will begin to happen that will alarm at least one of them to the fact that not is all it appears to be. Have the players make a percentile roll against ¼ of their I.Q., with the player who succeeds by the largest margin being the only player to notice what happens. If no player succeeds, continue having them make these checks every day until someone does.

The player who makes a successful check against ¼ of his or her I.Q. will be working in one of the workshops when the following scenario happens: He or she is given an electrical shock in the head, and shortly thereafter, sees that one of the other inmates has tentacles (or is blue, or some other out of the ordinary physical feature). This view lasts for but a moment, as the character is given another electrical shock to the head, and then all is normal again. Note that these are not the same electrical shocks that are given to inmates for poor behavior – these are a sign that the Crown is beginning to malfunction.

If the player who receives the shock reaches up to his head to feel/massage the area that was shocked, grant him a percentile roll against half his I.Q. Should this check succeed, the player will temporarily feel the metallic Crown on his head, but this will only last for a moment before everything feels normal again. In this scenario, award that player an additional 100 Experience Points for feeling the Crown early.

As time in the prison progresses, the player will start to see all kinds of things that he thinks are strange – aliens, mutants, robots, energy blasts from other inmates' hands and eyes, and all manner of different uses of super abilities. Each of these visions will last but a mere moment or two, and each will be preceded and followed by the electrical shocks that are an indication of the Crown malfunctioning.

Also as time progresses in the prison, all of the players will have the opportunity to overhear different conversations that the guards are having with one another. Some of the conversations will mention the Crown (only in name), others will mention how they want to be on solid earth, and others will be talking about how they are proud to work for such a wonderful corporation. Players should take all of these conversations to heart, as they are all clues to where they are and what is going on. Any player who figures out one of the following should be awarded an extra 100 Experience Points:

- Overhearing a conversation about the Crown and feeling his head or making the connection to something worn on the head;
- Overhearing a conversation about being on solid earth and making the connection that it means they want to be on Earth (or that they aren't currently on Earth);
- Overhearing a conversation about this being a wonderful corporation and making the connection that they aren't in the normal prison system, but instead are in a facility run by a private company.

Simply stating that this is all ConGenix is not enough to get the Experience Point award. The players already have a hate/hate relationship with ConGenix, and figuring out that this is the work of that particular corporation isn't all that hard to do. The clues above should be dropped very carefully and very subtly so as to lead the players along, but very slowly.

Eventually, the Crown on the player who is seeing all of the strange stuff will completely malfunction. When this happens, the player will receive the electrical shock that is for behavioral problems, but this time is not allowed a saving throw as the force and duration of the shock are quite beyond what is normally doled out. The player will be rendered unconscious for 1D10+10 minutes, and this will happen while he is in his cell. The Crown has completely malfunctioned, and is no longer working.

When the player regains consciousness, he is overwhelmed by a flooding of his memories returning, mixing with the memories he has of the prison he is in. Read the following to the player:

> *You awaken in your cell, having been forced into unconsciousness earlier by a shocking sensation running through your head. Your head is swimming slightly, but you feel different. You are groggy, your head doesn't hurt as much, and you are starting to remember things that have happened to you.*
>
> *Your mind is flooded with images and sounds that appear to have been repressed. Your arrest at ConGenix comes back shockingly fast. You remember that you were knocked out upon being arrested, and you scan your memory to see if you can remember what happened after that. And then you do.*
>
> *Your trial all comes back to you. A judge, a jury, a prosecutor all arguing over what to do with you. You get the feeling that the trial wasn't real, and you remember com-*

plaining about not having a defense lawyer present. You remember being forced onto a shuttle, but unconsciousness overtook you before you could see where you were going.

You remember landing, and then being swept through a doorway. They dragged you into a security room, sticking you with needles to draw your blood and take tissue samples. You remember being fitted with some type of headgear...

And then the memories stop. It feels as though you were two separate people since you arrived at this place. Your personality, the thing that makes you who you are, was subdued and forced to be silent. They took your voice and made you obey. But now you know who you are. What you are. And you know that you need to get out of here before things back home get too far out of hand...

It is at this point that the player will really have some challenges ahead of him. He remembers now that he is a super-powered being, and he knows that he is being held against his will. He remembers the things that led up to his incarceration (starting with the attack at the Daley Center), and he remembers who he was friends with. Unfortunately for him, his friends don't know who they are. Yet.

The player will probably reach up to his head to feel around for the headgear he remembers being fitted for. When this happens, he will distinctly feel the Crown upon his head, and he will probably want to remove it. Remember that it takes a P.S. of 22 or more to remove it – the unit may have malfunctioned, but the magnets holding it in place still work.

The player now has a few options in front of him, and none of them will be very easy to accomplish. The first option is to help his friends remove the Crowns from their heads. The other players will not know what is going on, and they will not believe anything about having been fitted with some type of device that alters their memories. They will not believe in super abilities, and even if the player who is free attempts to use his powers to show them, the Crown will prevent them from seeing it. Furthermore, attempting to remove a Crown that is not malfunctioning has the following results:

1. The person who is wearing the Crown suffers the effects of the behavioral modification shock.

2. An alarm is raised within the prison at the central security office that a Crown is being tampered with.

3. All doors in the entire prison are automatically closed and locked, and will not be opened until the alarm is shut off.

Locked doors can be picked by any character with the skills of Pick Locks (standard skill check). Any character who has the skills Electrical Engineer, Locksmith, or Mechanical Engineer can attempt to pick the door locks, but at a -20% penalty.

Security guards will do a thorough sweep of the prison, checking each inmate to see that they are still wearing their Crowns. Crowns don't malfunction, so the guards never check to make sure that they are still working. As long as the inmates are wearing them, the guards believe that they are working. Players will need to continue to wear the Crowns and act as if they are still under their effects. If they are spotted without their Crowns, the whole prison goes into high alert, and the players will be forced to fight their way out of the prison.

The second option is for the players to continue pretending that they are still under the effects of the Crown, but to sneak into the security office (area 3) and disable the computer. This is a tricky situation, but has huge rewards:

1. The computer controlling the Crowns can be disabled, thereby shutting off all Crowns in the prison.

2. A map of the entire prison, to include the shuttle bay, can be accessed and printed off.

3. Information about the prison, including that it's being run by ConGenix and that it's using super-powered individuals as a power source, can be obtained.

4. Detailed files on every inmate can be obtained.

5. Detailed files on every staff member can be obtained.

The tricky part with this option is that there are 5 guards in the hallway in plain sight of the door to the office, with 4 guards on duty in the office. Getting into the office will be hard to do, and a diversion may need to be created for the player(s) to get in. Any player who is able to successfully get into the security office without being noticed by the 5 guards in the hallway should be rewarded with an additional 500 Experience Points.

If a diversion is created, there is a chance (01-25%) that 2 or 3 of the guards in the security office will go to investigate. This would leave only 1 or 2 guards in the security room, which would give the players better odds. It will be up to the players to determine what diversion to cause, and how to cause it. The players should be rewarded with 100 – 500 extra Experience Points depending on the plan they come up with.

In order to operate the computer and get any information out of it, one of the players must have the Computer Hacking skill, and a skill check is required. Players may also have any number of super abilities or psionic powers that may allow them to read machine information or hack into machines, and this is an acceptable way of obtaining the information.

The third option is, of course, to fight their way out of the prison. This can be done, but it will be very hard. The security guards far outnumber the players, and any players who rely on some type of hardware or mystical object will be sorely outgunned. The security guards are also highly trained, and will do everything they can to take the players out. The guards will form barricades at both ends of every hallway, with no fewer than 4 guards at each barricade. The remaining guards will sweep the prison, looking for the players and opening fire without warning.

No matter what the players decide to do, they will invariably have to go through and search the entire prison. It is a high probability that at least 1 player will need to retrieve his or her armor, weapons, mystical object, etc., and they will need to go to the upper level and into area 31 to do this. They will also probably need a map of the prison in order to find this area, as well as to be informed about the wall separating areas 1 and 2 on the ground floor.

The players will also probably end up getting to the basement level and doing a search of all of the rooms down there. This scene should be described as a super-hero's worst nightmare. Every globe contains a super-powered being who is being used to help power the prison. Players will be shocked by this turn of events, and they will want to help their comrades. Unfortunately, there is almost no way to help them all.

A search of the power room will turn up information about the globes and the cycle they are all on to provide power to the prison on one of the power monitoring computers. Players will learn that if more than 10 globes are turned off at one time, the prison power supply will be interrupted and the prison will shut down. This has the side effect of shutting down the globes and starting the 5 minute countdown to self-destruct. This is a fail-safe method to prevent a large number of the high-powered super-beings from escaping at one time. ConGenix would rather lose the entire facility than have anyone escape and talk about it.

This will put the players into a serious situation. They can save themselves, but they cannot save those in the globes. In fact, once someone is released from a globe, it will take them almost 24 hours to regain consciousness, and another 24 hours before they can move on their own. This is far too long for players to wait to escape.

Players may very well exit the prison without doing a thorough search, and may not come across what lies in the basement level. If so, then so be it. While it is not necessary for the players to find what lies down there, getting information about it will definitely help them later in the campaign.

If the players are able to escape through area 1 and into the shuttle bay without having to fight their way through, award them 500 Experience Points for not having to resort to violence, plus 1,500 Experience Points each for "subduing" the guards in the prison. If they end up searching the basement level and finding out what is going on down there, award them an additional 250 experience each. Should the players end up with any information about the prison in their possession (hard drives, printouts, etc.), award them an additional 500 Experience Points each.

No matter which scenario plays out above, the players will eventually get through the teleporter in area 1 to the shuttle bay. It is in here that the players will face their final test in the prison.

Give the players a few moments to scan the area, reminding them that there is only one shuttle here. Let them figure out that they will need someone to operate the launch mechanisms in area 68 so that they can pilot the shuttle out of there. As soon as they figure this out, two figures will step through the teleporter in a final, desperate attempt to stop them.

Darren McDaniels

6th Level Master Psychic/Psionicist
Attributes: I.Q. 21, M.E. 34, M.A. 17, P.S. 20, P.P. 20, P.E. 13, P.B. 8, Spd 36.
Hit Points: 40, **S.D.C.:** 41, **A.R.:** 4.
I.S.P.: 178
Save vs Insanity: +13
Save vs Psionics: +8
Save vs Psionics Target: 10
Trust/Intimidate: 45%
Combat: Attacks per Melee: 5
Damage: +5
Disarm: +2
Dodge: +7
Initiative: +2
Parry: +7
Pull: +3
Roll: +4
Strike: +5
Kick Attacks
- Flying Jump Kick (4D6)
- Jump Kick (6D6)
- Karate-Style (2D4)
- Roundhouse Kick (3D6)
- Snap Kick (1D6)
- Wheel Kick (2D6)

Critical Strike on an unmodified roll of 18, 19, or 20.
Healing
- Bio-Regeneration
- Calm Rage
- Induce Sleep
- Mask I.S.P. and Psionics
- Wound Transfer

Physical
- Ectoplasm
- Ectoplasmic Disguise
- Impervious to Cold
- Impervious to Fire
- Night Vision
- Telekinesis
- Telekinetic Leap
- Telekinetic Punch
- Teleport Object

Sensitive
- Machine Ghost
- Mind Block
- Object Read
- See the Invisible
- Sixth Sense
- Telepathy

Super
- Hypnotic Suggestion
- Insert Memory
- Mentally Possess Others
- Psi-Sword
- Mind Wipe

Education: Military
Skill Program 1: Military, Basic
- Athletics
- Climbing
- Hand to Hand: Basic
- Military Etiquette
- Running
- W.P. Assault Rifle
- W.P. Grenade
- W.P. Pistol

Skill Program 2: Military, Psychological Warfare Specialist
- Computer Operation
- Psychology
- Military Intelligence
- Research
- Sociology

Skill Program 3: Military, Officer
- Camouflage
- Demolitions
- Detect Concealment
- Find Contraband & Illegal Weapons
- Intelligence
- Interrogation
- Land Navigation

8 Secondary Skills
- Hand to Hand: Martial Arts
- Language: Russian
- Pilot: Truck
- Radio: Basic
- Recognize Weapon Quality
- T.V. & Video

Darren will be wearing a fragmentation vest (A.R. 13, 120 S.D.C.), and will be carrying a .45 ACP (4D6 damage). He will only use the .45 ACP if/when he runs out of I.S.P., and even then he will attempt to escape back through the teleporter to the prison area before using it. He will not allow himself to be captured or taken hostage, preferring to die as an officer of the prison and employee of ConGenix than to betray the corporation.

Justin Matthews
7th Level Mage (Mystic Study)
Attributes: I.Q. 22, M.E. 15, M.A. 21, P.S. 27, P.P. 21, P.E. 15, P.B. 15, Spd 7.
Hit Points: 57, **S.D.C.:** 51, **A.R.:** 4.
P.P.E.: 144
Combat: Attacks per Melee: 6
Damage: +12
Dodge: +8
Initiative: +2
Parry: +8
Pull: +2
Roll: +8
Strike: +5
Save vs Horror Factor: +3
Save vs Magic: +3
Save vs Possession: +2
Opponent Save vs Magic Target: 15
Trust/Intimidate: 65%

Kick Attacks
- Karate-style (2D4)
- Jump Kick (3D6x2)
- Roundhouse (3D6)

Critical Strike on unmodified roll of 18, 19, 20.
Paired Weapons

Level 1 Spells
- Blinding Flash
- Cloud of Smoke
- Decipher Magic
- See the Invisible

Level 2 Spells
- Befuddle
- Chameleon
- Darkness
- Fear/Horror Factor
- Invisibility: Simple
- Mystic Alarm

Level 3 Spells
- Armor of Ithan
- Energy Bolt
- Ignite Fire
- Paralysis: Lesser

Level 4 Spells
- Blind
- Carpet of Adhesion
- Charismatic Aura
- Energy Field
- Fire Bolt
- Magic Net
- Multiple Image

Level 5 Spells
- Circle of Flame
- Energy Disruption
- Escape
- Fly
- Horrific Illusion
- Sleep

Level 6 Spells
- Fire Ball

Level 7 Spells
- Heal Self

Level 8 Spells
- Locate
- Metamorphosis: Human

Level 9 Spells
- Havoc
- Monster Insect

Level 10 Spells
- Summon Shadow Beast

Education: Three Years of College

Skill Program 1: Cultist
- Lore: Aliens
- Lore: Cults & Sects
- Lore: Geomancy & Ley Lines
- Lore: Magic
- W.P. Knife

Skill Program 2: Physical
- Acrobatics
- Boxing
- Gymnastics
- Wrestling

8 Secondary Skills
- Astronomy
- Hand to Hand: Expert
- Literacy
- Photography
- Research
- W.P. Pistol
- Writing

Justin will cast Armor of Ithan as his first action in combat, and he will then attempt to cast Carpet of Adhesion as his second action. After this, he will cast spells to directly hurt the players. He is carrying a .45 ACP (4D6 damage), but he will only use this once he is out of P.P.E. Justin will not allow himself to be taken prisoner or hostage under any means.

Justin is a company man, through and through, and he will resort to terrible means to protect the company. If the battle is going badly for him and Darren, he will attempt to operate the launching mechanisms, sucking the players out into the depths of space. If both he and Darren are in dire straits and he is unable to accomplish this, he will attempt to make his way back to the prison and down into the power room. Once there, he will start the self-destruct sequence.

Both Darren and Justin will have security badges on their person identifying them as employees of ConGenix, as well as having patches sewn onto their staff uniforms that have the ConGenix logo on them. The players should have no trouble identifying this logo anymore as they have been going toe-to-toe with ConGenix for quite some time now.

Once the battle is over, the players may find themselves without the ability to operate the launching mechanism and/or flying the shuttle. If none of the players has the ability to fly a shuttle, another prisoner will make his way through the teleporter. He will be badly hurt, but he will tell them that he can fly the shuttle. One of the players will need to have a teleporting or dimensional travelling ability so that they can operate the launching mechanism and then get into the shuttle safely for takeoff. If this is the case, the prisoner will have a minor Energy Expulsion power. If none of the players has this ability, then the prisoner will have the major super ability of *Teleportation*, allowing him to both operate the launching mechanism and fly the shuttle.

Once in flight, the shuttle will indicate that its coordinates are pre-programmed to land at an airstrip just outside of Albuquerque, NM. The players will invariably want to change this, and they should be allowed to do so. The players will also want to talk amongst themselves, and they may even question the other prisoner. All he can say is that he got lucky in escaping, and was glad that he was able to hitch a ride with the players. He has no memory of why he was ever arrested in the first place.

If any of the following scenarios happened during their escape of the prison, the prison will be destroyed by the self-destruct sequence shortly after takeoff:

● Darren is allowed to escape back into the prison;

● Justin is allowed to escape back into the prison;
● The players inadvertently shut off more than 10 globes;
● The players attempted to hack the central security computer and failed by more than 10%;
● The players attempted to hack the power room computer and failed by any margin.

If the players are able to escape with any of the Crowns, this is a huge bonus for them: they will be able to prove (eventually) what is going on at the prison. Award the players with 200 Experience Points for every Crown that they escape the prison with.

To demonstrate how the Crowns function, either one of the players will need to be a Hardware character (any, other than a Weapons Expert), or they will need to have access to a contact that is a Hardware person (again, any, other than a Weapons Expert). They will also need a copy of the software from the prison that allows control over the Crown, and this is something they could have obtained from hacking into the central security room's computer. If they escape with a disk containing the software, or any type of printout of the software code, award the players a bonus of 500 Experience Points (total, not each).

Reproducing the software on a computer on Earth and mastering how it functions will take more time than the players will currently have, so they may need to go to one of their contacts who is still friendly to them to have them take a look at the Crown and see if they can figure out the finer details. The answer will always be "I'm not sure; I haven't ever seen something like this before," and they will be told there is no guarantee that it can be done.

To be continued...

Due to space limitations, the final two chapters of this adventure will appear in **The Rifter® #54**. Sorry for the added suspense!

The Ravages of Time

Optional Rules for Rifts®

By S. E. Gibbons

Malcolm woke with a start, the thunder of distant artillery a fading echo in his mind. He found himself lying on an uncomfortable table in a white... surgical room? There were medical instruments and monitors scattered along the walls. In one corner a nurse and a doctor, their backs to him, were conferring in quiet tones. Malcolm shook his head and tried to sit up, but something was holding his right arm to the table.

"Awake already, soldier?"

The doctor had turned to look at him. Lights danced across the chrome visor that covered the upper half of his face. A Cyber-Doc! A twinge of panic shot through Malcolm's chest as the man came to the table and began to undo the bindings holding his arm down.

"You'll want to take it easy for a day or two," the doctor said, "to give the neuro-links a chance to fully integrate with your nervous system. After that it shouldn't interfere with your magic."

Malcolm stared at his own frightened reflection in the Cyber-Doc's visor as the last strap fell away.

"There you go. So, how does it feel?"

Malcolm lifted his arm, transfixed by the sight of his new bionic forearm and hand. What had happened to him!?!

Have you ever wanted to play through the *Coalition Wars®: Siege on Tolkeen* series, but been daunted by the time it would take to play through the *entire* war?

As a Game Master I've always wanted to play the Siege on Tolkeen. It's a fun and awesome story, and I know my players would love it. The problem is, my gaming group only gets together one night a month, for four or five hours at a time, so running a sweeping campaign like the Siege on Tolkeen isn't really practical – it'd take a decade just to play through most of the events detailed in the first book.

The obvious solution, of course, is to take only one or two adventures from each of the books and run the players through them. This really isn't a campaign, though – more like a series of one-night adventures with no connecting storyline. And role playing is all about telling a story!

So what to do?

Enter the Ravages of Time table, a way to fill in the blank spots between each night's adventures. The table gives the players a chance to find out what happened to their characters while they were off-screen, so to speak. (Please note that, while the table is specifically tailored to a group of characters fighting for the Tolkeen army, it can easily be adapted for a group of freelance fighters or even a group fighting for the Coalition States. In fact, with a little work this table could be applied to just about any campaign in one of Palladium's modern and/or Mega-Damage game settings, including the Minion War series. Indeed, the basic concept can be adapted to a campaign in any game where there are extended gaps in the ongoing action, or even to stitch together several unrelated adventures to create one ongoing campaign!)

Implementing the Ravages of Time

To begin with, it's best to use the table at the end of a game session if at all possible, as this gives the players a chance to make adjustments to their character sheets before the next game session. For a touch more fun, the players can even try to come up with a story explaining what happened to their characters based on the result rolled on the table. This can be especially fun when explaining how a character that was down on his luck at the end of the last game session now suddenly has major credits to spend, a shiny new vehicle or cybernetic limb! Remember, role-playing is all about telling a good story. Play around with it! Rolling on the table at the end of the game session also gives the G.M. time to consider the implications of what each player rolled with regard to the ongoing campaign. If this isn't possible (i.e., the current adventure finished up in the middle of the game session), it would be a good idea for the G.M. to pause the game for five to ten minutes to give everyone time to adjust their character sheets and to give himself time to reflect.

The players should each first roll 2D6 x 1,000 for the base amount of Experience Points their characters earned since the last adventure the group played through (the G.M. may want to increase or decrease the number of dice rolled if the amount of time passing is especially short/long). Next, have them roll on the following table to determine what happened to their character. Please note that almost every incident has a listing for additional Experience Points gained. Add this Experience Point bonus to the base amount of Experience Points rolled earlier, as applicable. These additional points represent what the character learned from the specific circumstances listed in the incident rolled.

01-03% Nothing of Consequence Has Happened. Hey, in the middle of a war this really isn't that bad. It's boring, but safe. Enjoy your good fortune while you have it! *Experience Point Bonus:* None.

04-06% Minor Injuries. The player character is suffering from minor injuries received either from a recent mission or possibly a friendly brawl at the local pub. Reduce S.D.C. or M.D.C. by 10%, and reduce all combat bonuses by -1 due to stiffness and sore muscles. The character will heal in the standard amount of time with no scars or disfiguring. *Experience Point Bonus:* +100.

07-09% Medium Injuries. Same as above, but the injuries received are more severe. Reduce S.D.C. or M.D.C. by 30%, and all combat bonuses by a third. The character also loses one attack per melee due to lingering pain, stiffness and sore muscles. *Experience Point Bonus:* +250.

10-12% Major Injuries! Same as above, but the injuries received are more severe. Reduce S.D.C. by 75% and Hit Points by 50%. If an M.D.C. character, reduce overall M.D.C. by 70%. Due to the severe nature of the injuries the character loses all combat bonuses. Also reduce attacks per melee by half until the character can fully heal. Better be careful out there on the battlefield! *Experience Point Bonus:* +400.

13-15% Loss of a Minor Limb. Roll percentile dice again. 01-50% means loss of one foot; 51-100% means loss of one hand. Player chooses which one (left or right). Limb has been replaced by basic cybernetic equivalent free of charge; magic players can opt to have a new Bio-System replacement if they had the funds to have paid for one-half of the procedure. (**Note:** This may not be an option later on in the war as shortages take hold – G.M.'s option.) If the player opts not to have a replacement limb or can't get one due to wartime shortages, be sure to apply any applicable negatives to the character's abilities that might be affected. In all cases, enough time has passed that the character has physically recovered from the injury, though there may be psychological issues to be dealt with. For Partial and Full Conversion Cyborgs (as well as characters impervious to cybernetic/bionic implants), ignore this result and re-roll. *Experience Point Bonus:* +1,000.

16-18% Loss of a Major Limb. Roll percentile dice again: 01-40% means loss of one leg, 41-80% means loss of one arm and 81-100% means the loss of one eye – player chooses which one (left or right). See Loss of Minor Limb above for details about possible replacement. For Partial and Full Conversion Cyborgs (as well as characters impervious to cybernetic/bionic implants), ignore this result and re-roll. *Experience Point Bonus:* +1,800.

19-21% Major Cybernetic Reconstruction! Due to life-threatening injuries the character received during a recent mission, he has been rebuilt as a Partial Conversion Cyborg! All four limbs have been replaced (player may opt to keep one arm, at G.M.'s discretion), along with spinal reinforcement and 1D4+1

internal organs replaced; all are basic, off-the-shelf systems without enhancements. Further implants/modifications may also have been performed at the time of the conversion (player's decision with G.M. approval, but only if the character had the funds to pay for them at the time). And yes, this does mean the character is now a partial cyborg, with all attendant changes to the character's O.C.C. entailed. This will be a traumatic experience for any character, but especially for magic wielding characters; G.M.s may opt to have the player roll on the Random Insanity Table found on page 332 of **Rifts® Ultimate Edition**. For player characters who are already Partial or Full Conversion Cyborgs (as well as characters impervious to cybernetic/bionic implants), ignore this result and re-roll. *Experience Point Bonus:* +4,000, and apply the total toward the new O.C.C.

22-24% Minor Scarring. Due to injuries received in the line of duty (but now fully healed), the character now has a minor scar on a prominent portion of his body, i.e. face, neck or hands. Reduce P.B. by one point. *Experience Point Bonus:* +400.

25-27% Medium Scarring. Same as above, except the injuries, and therefore the scars, were more severe. Reduce P.B. by 1D6+1 points. *Experience Point Bonus:* +600.

28-30% Major Scarring. Same as above, except the injuries, and therefore the scars, were truly horrific. The character probably spent some time in a hospital. Reduce P.B. to 1D4+2 and M.A. by 1D6. This could be a very traumatic event for a character who had a high P.B. to begin with, or whose race is naturally beautiful. At the G.M.'s discretion, the player may have to roll on the Random Insanity Table found on page 332 of **Rifts® Ultimate Edition**. *Experience Point Bonus:* +1,100.

31-33% Minor Alignment Change: Drop. The horrors of war have tarnished the character's outlook on life, making him a bit more cold and insensitive toward his fellow man. The character's alignment drops by one level. If Diabolic already, ignore this result and re-roll. *Experience Point Bonus:* +300.

34-36% Major Alignment Change: Drop. Participating in the ongoing horrors of the war has severely corrupted the character's spirit, making him much more cold and brutal. The character's alignment drops by three levels. If the character is Aberrant or Miscreant evil already, drop the alignment to Diabolic. If Diabolic already, ignore this result and re-roll. (Players should remember that just because someone is evil, it doesn't make him a mad-dog killer or butcher. Then again, they are in a war.) *Experience Point Bonus:* +600.

37-39% Minor Alignment Change: Rise. The hardships of war have awakened the character to what is important in his life, inspiring him to be a bit better of a person. Raise alignment by one level. If the character is already Principled, do not alter the alignment, but do add the Experience Point bonus and do not re-roll. *Experience Point Bonus:* +500.

40-42% Major Alignment Change: Rise. The kind act of a stranger or a friend's sacrifice amidst the hardships of war has recently touched the character's heart, rekindling his spirit to new brightness. Raise the character's alignment to one of the two good alignments (player's choice). If the character is Scrupulous already, raise the alignment to Principled. If Principled already, do not alter the alignment, but do add the Experience Point bonus and do not re-roll. *Experience Point Bonus: +1,000.*

43-45% Total Alignment Change: Reversal. The character has experienced an event so traumatic that it has changed his entire perspective on... well, everything. Players of good aligned characters must choose an evil alignment. Players of evil aligned characters must choose a good alignment. Players of selfish aligned characters must roll on percentile dice: 01-50% choose a good alignment, 51-100% choose an evil alignment. *Experience Point Bonus: +1,500.*

46-48% Heroics. The player character has engaged in some type of heroic action that saved the lives of a small group of civilians. The group's gratitude knows no bounds and they will help the character in any way they can in the future (G.M.'s discretion on available help, but remember that these people are probably refugees, so their efforts are limited to no more than some important piece of information, a hot meal, or maybe minor contributions toward paying for healing or repairs to the character's equipment). *Experience Point Bonus: +1,000.*

49-51% Major Heroics. The player did something on a recent mission that helped the nation of Tolkeen as a whole. Because of this, a high ranking government official has taken notice of the player character and may provide him with help or favors later on. This could range anywhere from helping the character obtain a new suit of power armor for free, to paying for or performing a Restoration spell on the character when needed. The exact nature of the help or favor is left up to the discretion of the G.M., and this is most likely a one-time thing. The reward might also be limited by what stage the war is in and any current supply shortages. *Experience Point Bonus: +2,000.*

52-54% Insanity. The horrors of war have pushed the character beyond his capacity to endure. Roll once on the Random Insanity Table found on page 332 of **Rifts® Ultimate Edition** to determine which insanity to apply to the character. This is a normal (non-magical) mental illness and can be treated as outlined in the rules. *Experience Point Bonus: +400.*

55-57% Minor Score. On the character's most recent mission he hit pay-dirt, finding a valuable item he was able to either trade in for a reward or sell. Increase the character's credits by 2D6x100. *Experience Point Bonus: +100.*

58-60% Major Score. As above, only the item was of greater value. Increase the character's credits by 1D6x1,000 +10,000. *Experience Point Bonus: +250.*

61-63% Score of a Lifetime! This is it, the big-time. The character either recovered an item of enormous value or bagged a fugitive with a HUGE reward on his head. Either way, the character just claimed his prize, 4D4x100,000 credits! This could be enough to retire on, but be careful; word of your character's sudden enrichment may make him a target himself. *Experience Point Bonus: +500.*

64-66% Loss of a Minor Valuable. During a recent mission the character lost something valuable to him (either destroyed in combat or stolen while in town/back at base). The G.M. selects one item from the character sheet to be erased. This could be a weapon, armor, article of clothing or any other physical thing that is listed among the character's possessions. *Experience Point Bonus: +200.*

67-69% Loss of a Major Valuable (or Several Minor Valuables). Same as above, except that the item was something major, like a magical weapon or a large portion of the character's credits (1D6x10+20 percent of total money). In the alternative, the character could lose several items of lesser value if he didn't have anything of major importance (G.M.'s discretion). *Experience Point Bonus: +300.*

70-72% Lost All Funds. The character either got drunk and had all his credits stolen or he lost them all gambling; player's choice. Either way the character needs to bum off of friends for meals and such until his next payday. In the alternative, he could try selling some of his possessions. *Experience Point Bonus: +350.*

73-75% Lost Everything but the Shirt Off Your Back! The character's quarters/house/apartment was damaged while he was out on a mission. The destruction could have been caused by a bomb, a riot, a natural fire or rampaging monster (G.M.'s choice). Everything the character had left behind was completely destroyed! Only items actually carried by the character during a normal mission, including personal vehicles/riding animals/etc., were not lost – erase everything else from the character sheet. On the plus side, the character was carrying his credit card so he hasn't lost any money he may have had unless he habitually keeps it at home (e.g. hidden under a mattress, under a floorboard, etc.). *Experience Point Bonus: +500.*

76-78% Despise the Supernatural. An event during a recent mission has instilled a strong and abiding prejudice in the character against supernatural creatures (if the character is a supernatural creature, then the prejudice is against ordinary mortals). This might have been coming across some monsters torturing an innocent person, or having a supernatural being pick on the character. For whatever reason, the character now finds it difficult to work with or even be civil toward supernatural beings. This may lead to refusal to work with a supernatural teammate, or attacking a supernatural ally over a minor disagreement. While not an obsession, this dislike is so powerful that the character might react irrationally in the heat of the moment. Also dislikes Shifters and any other mortal who calls upon the supernatural for empowerment (Warlocks, Witches, etc.). *Experience Point Bonus:* +400.

79-81% Promotion! The character did something good on a mission that caught his commanding officer's eye. To reward such exemplary behavior, the character's rank has been advanced one level, with attendant honors and higher pay grade. Add 1D6x1,000 credits to the character's total. *Experience Point Bonus:* +400.

82-84% Demotion! The character did something stupid on his last mission that came to the attention of his commanding officer. As a consequence, the character has lost rank, with attendant loss of honor/esteem and pay grade. Roll 1D6x100 and subtract from the character's credits as an additional fine! *Experience Point Bonus:* +400.

85-87% Received Word: Good. Your character has just received word that a close member of his family (or beloved friend) who was presumed killed early in the war is alive and well inside Tolkeen City! The great news has put your character on a temporary high: +10% to all skill rolls and +1 to strike, parry and dodge for 1D4 days. *Experience Point Bonus:* +100.

88-90% Received Word: Bad. Your character has just received word that a close family member (or beloved friend) who was presumed safe in Tolkeen City has been killed (either in combat or some random murder/accident). The bad news throws your character into a bit of a funk: -5% on all skill rolls, -2 to initiative and -1 to strike for the next 1D4 days. (**Note:** The penalties for receiving bad news are not as severe as the bonuses for good news since the character is in a war and somewhat used to hearing of tragic deaths.) *Experience Point Bonus:* +250.

91-93% Won a New Vehicle! The character, either through gambling, a one-on-one contest or pure, random chance ("You are our one-millionth customer!") has just won a brand new vehicle! This could be a hovercycle, riding animal, car or truck. Most likely it won't be a military vehicle or anything too expensive (G.M.'s discretion as to what the vehicle will be) but hey, it's free! *Experience Point Bonus:* +100.

94-96% Just Returned From R&R. The character has just gotten back from a great visit home. He is rested, refreshed and ready to go. The character enjoys a +1 to all saving throws for the first two days of the new adventure. Additionally, the character can do strenuous labor/exercise/combat for twice as long as normal before feeling the effects of fatigue, also for the first two days of the adventure. *Experience Point Bonus:* +200.

97-99% Re-Roll on the Table Twice. Similar or identical results can either be cumulative or re-rolled; G.M.'s discretion. Both Experience Point bonuses are added to the base points.

100% Death. The character has died on a recent mission. Sorry, roll up a new character. But hey, at least your character gave up his life heroically, fighting for the good of oppressed people everywhere! *Experience Point Bonus:* Um, it's sort of pointless, don't you think?

A Few Final Thoughts

Game Masters, as you use this table, don't overlook the many adventure opportunities that the events listed could precipitate or how it could affect your next planned adventure. Remember, every action creates a reaction and all choices and events *do* have consequences down the road.

Also remember that not all people agree on what they think is fun. I do have some players who, as part of their personal playing style, would rather not roll on a random table for anything, especially when DEATH is on the line! For those players I offered the following option: Nothing happens to the player's character during the time between adventures, but the total Experience Points earned during his "off screen" time is only 1D6x100 points. This lesser amount of Experience Points is representative of their characters having hung back from the action, not taken risks and basically done their best not to attract attention during that time period.

Last but not least, some players, after reading through some of the more dramatic items listed on the table, may feel that such changes are best role-played instead of being arbitrarily assigned from a random-roll table. This is a valid concern. There are quite a few detrimental items on the table – this is deliberate, as the realities involved with being part of a protracted war mean that oftentimes even good people end up suffering. Game Masters should solicit and take into consideration their players' opinions before introducing this table into their games. If there are items or events in this table that make you or your players uncomfortable, please feel free to re-roll to get a different result, alter the item in question or even remove it altogether from the table. Just remember that this table is meant to be a fun and helpful tool that enables G.M.s and players to play through sweeping campaigns like the *Siege on Tolkeen* or the *Minion War™* series, not a shackle that takes the fun out of your game.

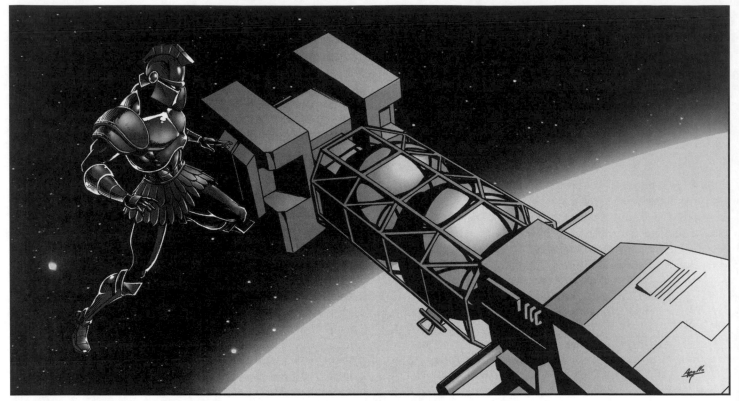

The Hammer of the Forge™

Chapter Fifty-Three:

"The Two Vulcans"

By James M. G. Cannon

Returning to the cold blackness of space felt like coming home. Sheathed within his crimson and black centurion armor, Caleb Vulcan allowed himself a small smile. A Knight of the Cosmic Forge, Caleb relished the opportunity to explore the infinite reaches of space, whenever he had the chance. A brief respite from a very hectic schedule allowed him to don his armor and blast off for parts unknown. Or at least the relatively quiet parts of space around the planet Alexandria, in the heart of the United Worlds of Warlock.

Caleb enjoyed the solitude, the emptiness, the quiet. The stars, jewels of light, hinted at the infinity of worlds available to explore. Sometimes, he had to remind himself that he wasn't giving up all of this freedom. He supposed that all bridegrooms felt the same way on the night before their wedding, even if they did not possess the same canvas upon which to pin their hopes and fears.

Just then the crackle of an incoming call appeared on his comm unit. Caleb tongued the receiver to life, and a distress call from the freighter *Veil of Night* came through. Caleb frowned. He hoped this wouldn't make him late getting back to Alexandria, but he had responsibilities as a Knight. Among them was looking out for people in trouble.

"*Veil of Night*, this is Caleb Vulcan, Cosmo-Knight. I am near your position and approaching at best possible speed. Hang tight, we'll get you out of trouble yet."

The only response from the freighter was a repeat of the distress message. An automated call, then, which could mean any of

a billion problems. Caleb altered his course and aimed his scarlet form towards the freighter.

Within an hour, Caleb caught sight of the ship. A three hundred tonner of modular manufacture, it looked relatively unharmed. But it was drifting. Caleb tried contacting the ship again, receiving the same message. He circled the ship, saw no sign of exterior damage, and all the escape pods seemed to be in place. No crew members were visible through any of the windows. The bridge looked deserted.

Caleb found an airlock in the middle of the freighter. To his surprise, the lock cycled open as he approached. Cautiously, Caleb entered the airlock. He tried the comm again, but no answer came. Caleb smelled a trap, but felt compelled to investigate further. Air slowly filled the small chamber and the inner door opened, allowing Caleb access to the ship. Caleb saw a bare hall, lit with emergency lights, empty of sapient beings.

He keyed the radio on the bulkhead. "This is Caleb Vulcan, Cosmo-Knight. I am investigating your distress call. Is there anyone aboard?"

The radio crackled. "Radiation leak," a weak voice said. "Unable to lock it down. Crew sickened. Need help." Then static.

Something at the back of Caleb's neck itched. He didn't like this, not at all. Still, he checked the bulkhead for deck plans, a computer terminal, something of use. As he took a few steps down the corridor, he felt the ship lurch under his feet, and the heavy grinding of mechanical components unlocking. Without thinking, Caleb spun, unleashing a flash of crimson light from the visor of his helm that burned through the airlock door behind him. He launched himself through the opening, shattering the exterior door, and hurtled into space just as the ship detonated. The silent explosion hammered into Caleb, knocking him around and sending him spinning through space.

He stopped himself, armor battered but body whole. From upside down he watched as the front section of the craft, having detached before the bomb went off, slowly came about. Hidden panels opened up, revealing two batteries of grav guns and a bank of missile launchers. The guns tracked Caleb as he oriented himself and rocketed towards the ship. He juked and weaved, dodged and dove, as projectiles roared soundlessly past him. The missile bank came to life, but in seconds Caleb flew well within their minimum range. He aimed himself at the bridge windows and accelerated.

The glass, harder than most metals, shattered as Caleb's hurtling body connected with it. The blast shields dropped almost immediately, keeping life and atmosphere within the bridge, but Caleb made it all the way through.

Two humanoids sat at the controls, but jumped up as Caleb appeared. The Wulfen, in full environmental armor decorated in whirls of Wulfen Runes, jumped back from the weapons console and quickly drew a Vibro-Axe. The other, a humanoid of indeterminate race underneath his full suit of protective gear, drew a pair of pistols, but seemed hesitant to actually fire.

Caleb lighted on the floor of the bridge and surveyed his two would-be assassins. "Nice trap," he said. "Now what is this all about?"

In answer the Wulfen snarled and leapt forward, bringing the axe down. A beam of red energy appeared in Caleb's right hand, coalescing into the huge hammer that was his chosen weapon. The hammer's haft blocked the axe neatly, and a light push from Caleb sent the Wulfen sprawling.

The humanoid raised his pistols for a moment, then threw them to the floor. He held his hands up with a shrug. "I guess I'd like to make it to magistrate with all my bones intact."

"An excellent choice," Caleb said. He looked at the Wulfen, clumsily getting to his feet. "And you?"

With a snarl, the Wulfen dropped his axe.

Caleb dispelled his hammer. He gestured for the two sapients to sit down. He took the pilot's chair for himself and began laying in a course to the nearest UWW space station. "So, anyone want to tell me what all of this was about?"

* * *

"Bounty hunters?" Doctor Abbott said. In his dry British accent, the words sounded extra incredulous. "What would bounty hunters want with you?" Abbott was a shadowy being, not wholly material, his only features a pair of glimmering orange eyes. Normally he wore a battered trench coat and fedora, but now he stood in a black tuxedo with a red bow-tie.

"Apparently there's a price on my head," Caleb said. He turned away from the mirror where he checked the tying of his own black tie and looked into Abbott's glowing eyes. The two of them stood in the middle of Caleb's room at the home of Orestes and Penelope Acherean. The Atlantean nobles, friends of theirs and parents to their friend Kassiopaeia, insisted that the wedding be performed at their spacious home. Caleb and Romana could not refuse.

"From whom?" Abbott asked.

Caleb shook his head. "I don't know. The Tracers were expecting a payoff on Phase World. I'm guessing Thraxus, but I've no proof."

Abbott's eyes flickered. "Unlikely. It's not his style." Abbott paused. "You don't look terribly distressed."

"Should I be?" Caleb smiled. "I'm getting married today to the most beautiful, amazing woman in the Megaverse. A couple of desperate thugs aren't really that important."

Abbott chucked Caleb on the shoulder. "That's my lad. I tell you what, while you two are off on holiday, the gang and I will check things out. Look under rocks and such, see what scurries out."

"I'd appreciate that." Caleb stuck his hand out, which the shadowmage gamely took. "Thank you, Doc. Thanks for standing up for me in the wedding."

"It is a singular honor, Caleb. Besides, you've finally admitted that I am the best man." Caleb laughed, and Abbott's eyes twinkled. "Well, I will let you get to it. Don't take too long finishing up. We expect you in the great hall in twenty minutes. Sharply now!"

Abbott left. Caleb turned back to the mirror.

How long ago had that drive in his old dune buggy been? He spun out, flipped it, and the gas line had cracked. Just before the flames took the whole car, the Cosmic Forge had found him. Brought him to this strange place filled with danger, injustice, and horror. He was lucky to have people like Doctor Abbott around him. He hoped they would always be there, and silently promised to himself that he would always be there for all of them.

As Caleb reached for the black mourning coat draped across the bed, the room lit up. Flickers of electricity like lightning flashed across the bedchamber. Instantly, Caleb took a defensive stance. His armor wrapped itself around him with a crimson glow.

A crack appeared in the air before him, widening by the second, and a cold, silver sphere the size of a car slid out of it with a crash and caromed across the room. Caleb leapt out of the way as the device rolled past him and crushed the bed under its weight. Composed of a shiny metal, Caleb saw that it was not entirely spherical, but slightly ovoid, and covering in a rime of frost. Steam rose from the thing's surface as the room's heat went to work on it.

Caleb watched, curious but not yet concerned, as a sliver opened in the sphere. A doorway, widening perceptibly. A figure in red and black armor wedged itself through the opening and crashed to the floor. Caleb made no move to help the figure to his feet, waiting patiently. He had learned to expect the unexpected. This could be another attack, but it didn't feel like one. Somehow this all felt strangely familiar.

The figure staggered to his feet. Rime and frost layered his full environmental suit, and he moved stiffly. The pommel of some weapon peaked up over his right shoulder, and with a start Caleb recognized it. Just to be sure, he summoned his hammer into his hands, yet when he felt the normally comforting weight settle into his palms, he began to feel anxious.

"Who are you?" he said.

The figure held up a hand, asking for a moment. Then he went to work unlocking the seals on his helmet, and after a moment, pulled it free. The face that greeted Caleb was as familiar as his own – pale skin, strong features, blue eyes, shock of red hair – because it was his own. But this Caleb looked at least a dozen years older, haggard and worn out.

"This must be a shock," the other Caleb said.

"That's a TimePod," Caleb said, pointing at the sphere with his hammer. "And you're from the future."

"Okay, not so much of a shock. I don't think I ever noticed how annoying that can be." The other Caleb held up his hands. "I haven't much time. I have a lot to explain."

"I'm sure you do."

"You're taking this all pretty well," the other Caleb said.

"I've traveled through time on a few occasions myself. My, well I guess *our*, fiancée wears the Singularity Watch. I'd think it more surprising if this sort of thing didn't happen once in a while. So what brings you here on the night of my wedding?"

The other Caleb sighed. "A lot happens in the next ten years. Almost all of it bad. And the tipping point is tonight. Something is going to happen that sets into motion a decade of misery for you, the people you love, and the Three Galaxies as a whole."

Caleb dispelled his hammer and willed his armor away. Flickers of memory swam before his eyes, dim figures barely seen. A memory or a dream? "What are you talking about?"

"You remember that day in Arizona. When we flipped the dune buggy."

"And the Forge contacted us."

"The Forge offered us a choice – to stay on Earth, maybe survive the crash, probably end up in Vietnam, who knows what. Or to take up the mantle of the Cosmo-Knight, and get to fly around in space and catch bad guys, like we'd always dreamed of doing. Hardly a choice, right? But after we accepted, the Forge gave us glimpses of our future, warning us what we had gotten ourselves into."

Caleb blinked. "I remember. Sort of." The flickers behind his eyes gained substance and form, and he remembered –

– He saw a man in green, with a wolf's face and a shimmering axe held in one claw-like hand. There was a towering woman in silver, and she was kissing Caleb on the forehead. A giant of metal and flesh bellowed as it shattered a building with one swipe of its arm. A hive of otherworldly creatures bubbled over a man of red steel, drowning him in bodies. A starship skimmed the edges of a black hole, daring destruction on a sacred mission. Beneath the sea, beneath light and air, Caleb held a blade of fire that would not extinguish, and used it against a tentacled monstrosity that devoured whales and submarines as Caleb wrestled it. And there, Caleb stood in chains, the marks of his rank stripped from him, his eyes dead and weary. A thin boned man with the ears of an Elf laughed, and his fine fingered hands closed about the throat of Caleb's wife. An army of mechanical creatures tore apart a world, piece by piece, while Caleb watched immobile.

Some of these things had come to pass, and many had not. But one of them stood out.

"Harkonnen is going to kill Romana."

Caleb looked his other self in the eye, and suddenly knew what sparked ten years of misery. "Tonight?"

"Harkonnen is on his way," the other Caleb said with a sigh. "He's made an alliance with Geryon, the Kreeghor noble whose plans you destroyed. They're the ones who have put a price on your head. I think they wanted to soften you up, put you on your guard, but the wedding is too good a target to pass up."

Caleb took a step backward. "You... this happened to you. You saw him kill her."

The other Caleb nodded. There was a faraway look in his eyes, and yet they still dimmed with moisture. "I was too late to stop

him. So I killed him myself. And lost my right to call myself a Knight of the Forge."

The two of them stood there for a long moment as Caleb absorbed the revelations, and the other Caleb remembered.

Finally, the other Caleb spoke, his voice hoarse. "There can be no wedding. You have to leave, and leave as publicly as possible. Draw Harkonnen and his cronies away from Alexandria."

Caleb looked up. "No. We stay. We're prepared now. We can expect him, defeat him."

"Don't you think I've tried that?" the other Caleb said. "Do you think this is my first trip back in time? I've already tried a dozen times to stop him. This is the only thing I can think of to make it work. Make your choice quickly, Caleb. We're running out of time."

Caleb thought hard for a few moments. This felt too real to be a trick, but what if it was?

"What are my parent's names?"

"What?"

"My parents. No one in the Three Galaxies knows who my parents are. If you're really me, you'll know."

The other Caleb looked pained, but he said, "Master Gunnery Sergeant Ezra Vulcan married Deborah Ruth Sagan in 1949, when Debbie was three months pregnant with you. Ezra never wanted kids, but he manned up and did the right thing. Still, he couldn't resist naming you Caleb. Means 'dog,' in Hebrew, and he always said he would have rather had a dog."

"Only after Mom died," Caleb whispered.

"Do you believe me now?"

Caleb nodded.

Ten minutes later, Caleb pushed open the double doors that led into the main hall. The assembled guests turned to greet him, but everyone froze and grew silent as they registered his armor.

"There will be no wedding today," he said. "We are about to be attacked. Battle stations, everyone." While they reacted, all talking at once, and Doctor Abbott and Ariel stepped forward, demanding an explanation, Caleb lifted up off the floor and flew out of the building. He accelerated quickly, rising straight up into the air as soon as he reached the outside. He reached escape velocity quickly, exploding out of Alexandria's atmosphere and into the black.

He flipped his comm system on, ignoring the buzzing demands from below. He sent a broad message across all channels. "Harkonnen. I know you're there. If you want me, you'll have to come and get me."

At that, all chatter from below suddenly ended. Out of the corner of his eye, Caleb saw a ripple in space that resolved itself into a light attack cruiser. Harkonnen's ship decloaked, its weapons coming to bear on Caleb as it turned towards him. An incoming transmission pinged on Caleb's comm. Harkonnen's voice, with a taunting lilt: "I see you."

Caleb stoked the cosmic furnace within him and fled, blasting off for the outer planets in Alexandria's system.

* * *

Romana, dressed in white, swept into Caleb's abandoned apartments. Arwen had rushed from the main hall to inform her of the latest development, and through her shock and anger and hurt she had heard Caleb's broadcast. The Singularity Watch had not been part of her wedding ensemble, but she snatched it up after his declaration, and discovered something strange. A tem-

down her spine. "You are destined to die tonight. Murdered by a psychotic Elf. I'm here to stop that."

"By ruining my wedding and sending the man I love off to his death?"

The other Caleb's face hardened slightly. "Better me than you," he said.

"No, I do not accept that. Tell me everything, right now, or so help me, it will not matter to me who you are or who you were. My husband is out there alone and it's your fault."

The other Caleb shook his head. "I am so sorry, Romana." Suddenly his right hand was filled with a small, silver cylinder, and his thumb depressed a button. A spray of greenish vapor washed over Romana. She felt herself losing consciousness. Her fingers fumbled for the keys on the watch, but she went under almost immediately.

The other Caleb caught her as she fell. He scooped her up in his arms, and carried her towards the TimePod.

* * *

Caleb poured on the speed. Missiles exploded around him, as the craft began to gain on him. Harkonnen taunted him as Caleb dodged and weaved through space, trying to evade each attack. Caleb risked a glance behind him, and saw the docking bay open up. Four fighters blasted out of the ship.

Fragments of armor floated away from Caleb's body as explosions echoed soundlessly near him and shrapnel tore through him. He pushed himself further and faster, reaching his top sublight speed. The missiles dropped away, but the fighters and the cruiser stayed with him.

The last of the inner planets' orbital paths were left behind, and Caleb saw the big gas giant Thespia dead ahead. Immense rings of icesteroids encircled the planet. Caleb angled himself straight for them.

The fighters closed in. Grav cannons unleashed a spray of lethal bullets that were low velocity, easily evaded, but in such number that Caleb couldn't escape them all. A shoulder plate exploded into fragments. His crest split in two. And then he was in the midst of the icesteroids, and the cover helped. The cannon fire pulped the chunks of floating ice. Fragments exploded all around, caroming off one another, scattering through the rings.

"I'm coming for you, little Knight," Harkonnen's voice said in Caleb's ear.

The docking bay opened once more, and the slight form of the Elf, former Imperial Guardsman, shot into space. He was clad in a replica of his black and crimson Imperial armor, encasing him from head to toe. He wore a sword across his back.

Caleb dodged and wove his way through the icesteroids. He popped up into the path of a fighter and cut loose with his eyebeams, full power. They punched through the craft's minimal shields and fractured the cockpit. The craft spun out and into an icesteroid, exploding in a silent fireball.

The other three were on him in a second. Caleb ducked down behind a chunk of ice, and it disintegrated behind him.

"Leave off! He's mine!" Harkonnen ordered across the comm channel.

And then he was there, skimming off the surface of an icesteroid to slam bodily into Caleb. The two of them went spinning, whirling through ice and space. Caleb bounced off a rock, elbowed Harkonnen in the face, and brought his fist up into his side. Harkonnen's armor cracked, but he didn't feel the blows.

poral incursion had occurred only minutes before Caleb entered the great hall – an incursion that occurred in his room.

She saw and recognized the TimePod. Her eyes swept the room, but she still started as a figure stepped out from behind a curtain. It was Caleb, clad in unfamiliar red and black armor, his hammer over his shoulder, his face haggard and worn. The Singularity Watch pinged on her wrist.

"What is this about?" Romana said.

Caleb smiled, but the smile was bittersweet. "Time. The future. Fate. Visions. Destiny. The usual, in other words."

Romana crossed her arms. "What did you say to him?"

The other Caleb frowned. Slowly he approached, his hands open and held out, watching her intently. "Romana," he said. He said her name with such longing, such intensity, it sent a shiver

The Elf's fists flashed, hammering into Caleb's head and exposed shoulder. Caleb heard laughter on his comm.

"They say revenge is a dish best served cold," Harkonnen said, "but I prefer it hot, fueled by rage and fed on blood. Don't you agree?" He blocked Caleb's swing and smashed Caleb in the breastbone, knocking him backward. The stylized hammer image on his chest fractured.

A red bar formed in Caleb's hands, coalescing into his hammer. As Harkonnen leapt forward, Caleb swung it like a baseball bat. It connected with a silent crash, the impact traveling up Caleb's arms. Home run – Harkonnen spun away, and bounced off an icesteroid.

Caleb unleashed eyebeams, but the Elf drew his sword, and the glittering blade caught and deflected his blast. An icesteroid melted into fragments.

Harkonnen launched himself at Caleb, point first. Caleb turned him aside with the head of his hammer, and then had to spin the weapon quickly to block the rapid series of stabs and cuts that Harkonnen unleashed. Sparks of electricity flew off from the blade as it connected with Caleb's hammer.

"You can't stop me, Vulcan. I'm invulnerable. I never tire, and I'm stronger than you. You defeated me through luck last time. Then there's that little party to crash when I'm through with you. All your allies gathered together under one roof, just begging for an air strike. Think of what I'll do to that pretty little bride of yours!" Harkonnen laughed. He punctuated every word with a slash or cut, and Caleb could not deflect all of them. The weapon, clearly magical, burned like fire wherever it touched him, slipping easily between the gaps in his armor to score his flesh.

Caleb grimaced under his helmet. His eyebeams flashed, not at Harkonnen, but at the sword. His beams cut it in two, and the impact knocked it out of the Elf's hand. Momentarily off guard, Harkonnen took Caleb's hammer in the side of his head. The plates of Harkonnen's helmet cracked, and the glass in his visor shattered, revealing his cold white eyes.

Harkonnen's foot spun around into Caleb's midsection, and his hands flashed forward, hammering into Caleb's chest. Caleb knocked him away with the hammer. His eyebeams flashed, burning the Elf's armor, pushing him back, but still Harkonnen laughed.

Caleb swung the hammer, aiming for Harkonnen's head, but the Elf caught it with both hands. They struggled, but Harkonnen really was stronger, and he ripped the hammer from Caleb's hands. Harkonnen threw it away, then knocked Caleb into an icesteroid.

Harkonnen sprang forward, smashing into Caleb's chest. Fractures exploded across his breastplate. Harkonnen's fist and feet flew around, hammering Caleb. The Knight blocked and threw punches of his own, and though he broke off pieces of the Elf's armor, Harkonnen himself did not flag. And still the laughter rang in Caleb's ears, cold and mad.

Out of the corner of his eye, Caleb saw the point of Harkonnen's sword, floating over the Elf's shoulder. It still sparked with magical energy. Caleb smashed Harkonnen's face with an elbow, grabbed for the blade with his left hand. He felt the edge cut into his fingers as he wrapped them around, twisted, and drove the blade towards Harkonnen.

It sank into his left eye, neatly sidestepping his vaunted invulnerability. Harkonnen howled, knocking Caleb away.

"I'm not the same kid you fought all those years ago," Caleb said. His voice sounded hoarse in his own ears. "You've made a string of bad choices in your life, Elias. This is your last one."

The Elf plucked the blade from his eye, leaving a ruined socket behind. Crystallized droplets of blood floated in space. Light from the distant sun filtered through the rings, alighting them with molten fire. Fragments of ice and armor orbited the two combatants, and in the distance hovered the remaining three fighters. Behind them, outside the rings, the ominous presence of the attack cruiser waited.

"My fault for bringing the blade," Harkonnen said. He threw the shard of metal away. "That's your last shot, Vulcan. Time to die."

"Your helmet's cracked, Harkonnen. How are you speaking?"

The Elf's remaining eye narrowed. Caleb shot forward, his hammer suddenly in his hand, and the heavy weapon smashed Harkonnen across the forehead. The top of his helmet sheared off and spiraled away into space. Another swing shattered the rest of the faceplate. Beneath the helm, Harkonnen wore a half-mask that covered his nose and mouth. Coils fed back down along Harkonnen's neck, connecting to the armor's air supply.

Invulnerable to all but magic he might be, but the Elf still needed to breathe.

Harkonnen regained his equilibrium, catching the hammer again. He pushed it backwards, hate and bile radiating from his pale eye. Something that might have been fear flickered there, all but hidden.

Caleb unleashed eyebeams. The half-mask disintegrated, but the Elf's flesh wasn't touched.

Now real panic blossomed in Harkonnen's eye. His mouth opened and closed, gulping for air. He pushed Caleb away and flew up, trying to escape back to the safety of his starcraft. Caleb grabbed him by the ankle and pulled him back down. Harkonnen fought and kicked and punched, but his strength failed moment by moment, as the air left him. At last, Harkonnen held up his hands in supplication. His eye dimming, he mouth "Help me."

Caleb shook his head.

The vision of Romana, struggling feebly in Harkonnen's grip, flashed before his eyes. He would not let that happen. He would die before he let that come to pass. And he would – he knew what he was doing, knew the consequences for what he was about to do.

He reached up and wrapped his hands around Harkonnen's throat. He squeezed.

Harkonnen's eye bugged. He found some last desperate dregs of strength, grabbing at Caleb's wrists and struggling to peel him off. He punched feebly at Caleb's helmeted head, but his strikes were nothing close to full strength.

Gradually, Harkonnen weakened. His arms fell away.

Caleb held on. Even as his armor disintegrated around him, fading away. Even as the cosmic fire in his breast slowly died. Even as his own lungs began to strain for air, as the vacuum of space went to work on his suddenly human flesh and blood, freezing and burning him.

Caleb Vulcan murdered Elias Harkonnen, and for his crime, he lost his status as a Knight of the Cosmic Forge. Not for long, though. The cosmic void he loved so much would kill him in seconds.

Over his shoulder, unseen as Caleb's eyes dimmed, the attack cruiser drifted closer.